THE TOLEDO MUSEUM OF ART
FOUNDED BY EDWARD DRUMMOND LIBBEY

CATALOGUE

OF

EUROPEAN PAINTINGS

BLAKE-MORE GODWIN

TOLEDO, OHIO

1939

FOREWORD

THIS PUBLICATION departs somewhat from the normal museum catalogue. It is fully illustrated, for we feel that a picture worthy of mention merits more accurate description than words may give. It is subjective rather than objective, for we hold that it is the function of a museum to teach, and as we attempt in our educational program to indicate the aesthetic qualities inherent in the works under consideration, we have felt that we should do the same thing in brief in our catalogue.

The catalogue is intended to serve the visitor to the galleries, the student and the scholar. For the casual visitor it attempts to present interesting and readable information, but more particularly, through the illustrations, to help him refresh his memory of what he has seen when he is remote from the Museum.

For the student it endeavors to estimate the importance of each painter, to indicate his place on the family tree of art, to suggest the relative qualities of the various pictures, and to show in some measure why they are worthy of inclusion in museum collections, and in what respects they recommend themselves to his contemplation and study.

Factual data, particularly of exhibition, publication and previous ownership, is offered for such uses as the scholar may wish to make of it.

Artists have been grouped by nationality, and thereunder in approximately chronological order. In general each artist has been assigned to that country in which he has produced the greater part of his work. In this, however, we have not been wholly consistent, for we insist upon assigning Holbein to Germany rather than to England, although the subject of our own work by him alone would warrant doing the latter; we have retained Whistler for America; and in the case of some of the more contemporary artists, we have attached them to France because of their training and the nature of their work.

The Museum's collections have grown through both purchase and gift. The principal donors have frequently acquired paintings and presented them immediately to the Museum. They have also secured works for their private collections, which they have enjoyed in their own homes and subsequently placed in the Museum. Where the latter has been the case, we have so indicated by repeating the donor's name, and, when available, the dates of his private ownership, in the list of previous collections. The date following the name of the donor in the gift line is that of presentation to the Museum.

The Founder of the Museum, Edward Drummond Libbey, left a considerable portion of his estate to produce income for the acquisition of works of art, so that his collection might be forever a living one. Those works indicated as his gift and bearing a date subsequent to 1925 have been purchased from this fund.

There are undoubtedly some errors and many omissions in this volume, the omissions particularly in the lists of previous collections. It will be deeply appreciated if those into whose hands this catalogue may come will advise us of such errors as they may discover, or of such additional facts as they may possess in respect to the paintings here published.

While I acknowledge authorship, and accept full responsibility therefor, I am also deeply grateful for much aid from others. The President of the Museum, William A. Gosline, Jr., and Molly Ohl Godwin have tempered my native conservatism by their enthusiasms. Nell L. Jaffe has been of great assistance, especially in the verification of the references. Other members of the Museum staff, including Charlotte Page, Ruth Knapp and Felice Kozak have contributed helpful notes. The photographs from which the plates were made are the work of Lee MacDonough. Composition and typography was largely designed by Gene A. Schlagheck. Elinor Knoblaugh and J. Arthur MacLean read and helped revise the manuscript. Frank A. Seiberling, Jr. and Nell L. Jaffe have assisted in the final revision, and to them also has fallen the lot of correcting the proofs.

BLAKE-MORE GODWIN

December 1, 1938.

ITALIAN PAINTINGS

Bonaventura Berlinghieri	Madonna and Child
Luca di Tomme	St. Anthony of Padua
Lorenzo di Niccolo Gerini	Madonna and Child with Saints
Filippino Lippi	Adoration of the Child
Piero di Cosimo	Adoration of the Child
Angelo Bronzino	Cosimo de' Medici
Giovanni Battista Tiepolo	Head of an Old Man
Giovanni Antonio Guardi	The Holy Family

BONAVENTURA BERLINGHIERI   Active 1228-1274

ANTEDATING Giotto and even Cimabue, Bonaventura Berlinghieri was the son of a Milanese-born painter who worked exclusively in Lucca. Of three brothers, all painters, Bonaventura alone left signed works existing today. He signed and dated in 1235 the painting of St. Francis and six scenes from his life now in Pescia, and did some frescoes at Lucca in 1244. While his father seems to have worked in the Romanesque style, the characteristics of Bonaventura's paintings are predominantly Byzantine.

MADONNA AND CHILD

The attribution to Bonaventura Berlinghieri, which is purely tentative, has been suggested by Van Marle. Set against a gold background, Madonna in blue robe, now of a distinctly greenish cast, and light orange dress is seated on a formal throne, holding but not supporting the Child. Both face straight to the front. Drapery falls in formal calligraphic folds. Rigid formal balance, carefully measured disposition of color areas give to the painting the fine designed quality characteristic of Byzantine works. It was probably painted before 1250.

Tempera on walnut, $15\frac{5}{8}$ x $37\frac{1}{2}$ in. (40 x 95 cm.) Unsigned.
Gift of Edward Drummond Libbey, 1936.

COLLECTIONS: Count Ambrozzy-Migazzy; Austrian private collection.

REFERENCES: Van Marle, Some Unknown Tuscan Paintings of the XIIIth Century, Apollo, XXI (March 1935), 127 repr.; Comstock, Dugento Panel at the Toledo Museum, Connoisseur, XCVIII (Oct. 1936), 230-1, repr.; Parnassus, VIII (Oct. 1936), 20; Art News, XXXV (Oct. 19, 1936), 18-19, repr.; Art Digest, XI (Oct. 15, 1936), 17, repr.

LUCA DI TOMME 1330?-1392?

ONE OF the leading Sienese painters of the late trecento, his was the third name on the register of the Sienese Company of St. Luke when confirmed as a guild in 1355. Perhaps pupil of Barna da Siena, or of Simone Martini, his early works show the influence of Pietro Lorenzetti, his later that of Simone Martini. Upon types and proportions of the one, charm and delicacy of the other, he impressed his own personality, being of that order of artists content to build upon inherited foundations, to leave to others the future advancement of art through introduction of new ideas and ideals.

ST. ANTHONY OF PADUA

In tones quiet to somberness, against dull gold background, the panel, once part of a large altarpiece, shows strong feeling for design, dependence upon predecessors in concept and content. In the gable above Anthony of Padua is the smaller, more interesting figure of Anthony Abbot. The work may perhaps be dated between 1365 and 1375.

Tempera on wood, 15⅜ x 44 in. (39 x 112 cm.)   Unsigned.
Gift of Paul Reinhardt, 1925.

COLLECTION: Eduard Simon, Berlin.

REFERENCES: Berenson, Italian Pictures of the Renaissance, Oxford, 1932, p. 314, p. 709;   Berenson, Lost Sienese Trecento Paintings—Part IV, International Studio, XCVIII (Jan. 1931) 29-35, repr.;   Museum News, No. 63, Sept. 1932.

LORENZO DI NICCOLO GERINI 1376?-1440

SON AND pupil of Niccolò di Pietro Gerini, he with his father assisted Spinello Aretino. He followed the style of Giotto, diluted by transmission through Taddeo Gaddi or Spinello. Last adherent of the Giottesque tradition, he sought to hold to the principles of his illustrious predecessors, but could not avoid the trend of the fifteenth century.

MADONNA AND CHILD WITH SAINTS

Gothic in tradition, Giottesque in many details, decadence is evident throughout, though naive and charming simplicity remains. Difficult to date with any certainty, it may have been painted between 1410 and 1420.

Tempera on wood, 13 x 15¾ in. (33 x 40 cm.) Unsigned.
Gift of Mrs. Edward Drummond Libbey, 1935.

COLLECTION: Chester Johnson, Chicago.

PRATO his birthplace, son of Filippo Lippi, he was the pupil of his father, and of his father's pupil, Botticelli. Entrusted at twenty-seven with the completion of the frescoes in the Brancacci Chapel, he was influenced by the previous work thereon by Masaccio. Perhaps lacking some of the inventiveness of his great predecessors, he stands on the threshold of the sixteenth century, adherent of the old traditions, harbinger of the High Renaissance. Superior to all but the very greatest of his time, he approached nearer to the modern spirit than any other artist of the age. Unwilling to repeat himself, his works are not all of even quality, his later ones showing certain affectations, but each sounded a new note, anticipating the century to come.

ADORATION OF THE CHILD

Bright red of the Virgin's dress and rich blue of Her mantle, complementary red-purple and yellow-green of the kneeling angel's costume, felicitously combined with warm yellow-gray of Her skirt form especially beautiful contrast to the cool purple-grey of architecture and pale tints of landscape. Rich tapestry of designed foliage forms setting for the figures; distant view of Italian landscape seen through stately arch and piers enriches their background. Condition of the panel is impeccable, untouched save at the extreme edges since it left the artist's hands four hundred and fifty years ago. Of superb quality, it summarizes Florentine painting at the end of the fifteenth century, represents Filippino Lippi perfectly at the moment of his fullest capability, presents his innovations clearly, portrays his epoch truthfully. Probably painted about 1485, it is an outstanding example of tempera technique. As the first important Italian picture acquired by the Toledo Museum, it sets a high standard for all future additions in that field.

Tempera on wood, 29 x 32¼ in. (74 x 82 cm.) Unsigned.
Gift of Edward Drummond Libbey, 1930.

COLLECTIONS: Charles Timbal, Paris, 1851-1871; Gustave Dreyfus, Paris, 1871-1930.

REFERENCES: Reinach, Tableaux inédit et peu connus tirés de collections françaises, Paris, 1906, p. 28, Pl. XX, repr.; Van Marle, The Development of the Italian Schools of Painting, The Hague, 1931, XIII, 225, note (attr. to Mainardi); Tietze, Meisterwerke Europäische Malerei in Amerika, Vienna, 1935, p. 60, p. 327, repr.;

Scharf, Filippino Lippi, Vienna, 1935, p. 119, p. 212, repr. (attr. to Raffaelino del Garbo, No. 164.); Neilson, Filippino Lippi, Cambridge, 1938, pp. 213-14, repr. Fig. 108 (attr. to school of Filippino Lippi); Meyer, Die Sammlung Gustave Dreyfus, Pantheon, VII (Jan. 1931), 10-19; Art News, XXIX (Feb. 14, 1931), 3, repr.; Art Digest, V (Feb. 15, 1931), 1, 8, repr.; Pantheon, VII (March 1931), 120, repr.; Parnassus, III (March 1931), 52, repr.; Revue de l'Art Ancien et Moderne (Supplement), LIX (April 1931), 178; American Magazine of Art, XX (June 1931), 483, repr.; Museum News, No. 67, Dec. 1933, repr.; Connoisseur, XCIII (March 1934), 199, repr.; Children's Museum News, No. 7, March 1935, repr.

PIERO DI COSIMO 1462-1521

His PRODUCTIVE life divided equally between the fifteenth and sixteenth centuries, youthful assistant to Cosimo Roselli, Piero's chief artistic influence was that of Botticelli, transmitted, perhaps filtered, through Filippino Lippi. Profiting in technique from his contemporary, Lorenzo di Credi, and from his pupils Fra Bartolommeo and Andrea del Sarto, having broad acquaintance with art and literature of his own and earlier times, he was inventor, originator, man of fertile imagination, great versatility. Introducing innovations into his religious pictures, developing a whole world of fantasy all his own in secular and mythological subjects, he achieved a faultless technique, a smooth, almost polished finish in his paintings.

ADORATION OF THE CHILD

Among his masterpieces, greatest of his religious works, its artistry displays Piero's accomplishments, commands profound admiration. Sleeping Child, here appearing for the first time in Florentine art, and adoring Madonna dominate the composition, conform in curving lines to circular shape of panel. Luxuriant foliage in foreground, minute detail of village and pasture, receding view in background form effective, dignified setting, demonstrate sure linear and aerial perspective. Clear, cool colors, blue and blue-green, in sky and landscape set off deep blue cloak and red garment of Madonna, echoed in purple-blue of headdress, blue-purple of robe under Child, purples in roofs of village. Yellows in edges of book, Mary's hair, lining of cloak and Joseph's mantle, complete the primary triad. The painting may be dated about 1495. According to tradition it was given by Lorenzo de' Medici to a lady of the Guiducci family.

Oil on wood, diameter 63 in. (160 cm.) Unsigned.
Gift of Edward Drummond Libbey, 1937.

COLLECTIONS: Metzger (dealer), Florence; Alexander Barker, London; George Edmund Street, R.A., London; Arthur E. Street, London.

EXHIBITIONS: London, Burlington Fine Arts Club, Signorelli Exhibition, 1893, No. 17, catalogue p. 6, p. xvi; London, Royal Academy, Old Masters Exhibition, 1904, No. 33.

REFERENCES: Waagen, Treasures of Art in Great Britain, London, 1854, II, 126; Berenson, The Florentine Painters of the Renaissance, New York, 1909, p. 165;

Knapp, Piero di Cosimo, Halle, 1899, pp. 40-43, repr.; Crowe and Cavalcaselle, History of Painting in Italy, London, Hutton Edn., 1909, III, 63 (attr. to Signorelli), and note 3, 394, note 7 (attr. to Piero di Cosimo); Murray Edn., 1914, V. 88, note 3; A. Venturi, Storia dell' Arte Italiana, Milan, 1911, VII, i, 706; Van Marle, The Development of the Italian Schools of Painting, The Hague, 1931, XIII, 353; L. Venturi, Pitture Italiane in America, Milan, 1931, Pl. CCXVIII, repr.; L. Venturi, Italian Paintings in America, 1933, II, No. 288, repr.; Neilson, Filippino Lippi, Cambridge, 1938, p. 131, repr. Fig. 59; Philipps, Daily Telegraph, London, Jan. 2, 1904; The Times, London, Jan. 2, 1904; Richter, The Connoisseur, London, VIII (March 1904), 170, 174, repr.; Burlington Magazine, London, XXIX (Dec. 1916), 351, repr.; Museum News, No. 78, March 1937; Art Digest, XI (April 15, 1937), 12, repr.; Art News, XXXV (April 17, 1937), 14-15, repr.; Beaux-Arts, May 7, 1937, p. 1, repr.; Illustrated London News, C (May 29, 1937), 1004-5, repr.; Connoisseur, XCIX (June 1937), 343-4, repr.; Magazine of Art, XXX (June 1937), 360, repr.; London Studio, XIV (July 1937), 48, repr.; Fortune, XVII (Jan. 1938), 73, repr. in color.

ANGELO BRONZINO 1503-1572

NATIVE of Monticelli, suburb of Florence, Bronzino studied briefly with Raffaellino del Garbo and Pontormo. Painter of murals, panels, designer of tapestries, like most artists of his day, he was overcome by the glamor of Michelangelo, sought in emulation effects incompatible with his abilities. Lacking color sense, most necessary complement to his competence as draughtsman, his religious, allegorical, mythological works become cold, harsh. His reputation is established; he stands last of the great painters of the Florentine decadence by virtue of his splendid portraits, executed with distinction, notable for their beauty of surface texture.

COSIMO DE' MEDICI

Line, mass and color emphasize Cosimo's reserved, calculating, austere character. Against rich deep green of curtain shimmers steel-grey armor, accented by notes of red-orange. Sensitive, artistic hand lightly touches the helmet; an olive branch completes formal composition. Probably painted between 1546 and 1550, for he wears the Order of the Golden Fleece which was conferred in the former year, it is one of the finest of several repetitions of the same subject, now located in Cassel, in the Accademia, the Uffizi and the Pitti in Florence, in the Pinacoteca at Lucca, and the Metropolitan Museum, New York.

Oil on wood (transferred to plywood panel 1934), $30\frac{5}{8}$ x 41 in. (78 x 104 cm.) Unsigned.
Gift of Edward Drummond Libbey, 1913.

COLLECTION: Oscar Hainauer, Berlin, (sold 1906).

EXHIBITIONS: Bruges, Toison d'Or, 1907, No. 158, catalogue p. 47, (incorrectly described as on canvas); Toledo Museum, Portraits and Portraiture Throughout the Ages, 1937, No. 8.

REFERENCES: Vasari, Le Vite de' piu eccelenti Pittori, Scultori ed Architettori, Milanese Edn., Florence, 1879, VII, 598; Bode, The Collection of Oscar Hainauer, Berlin, 1906, p. 15, No. 68 (incorrect measurements); Schulze, Die Werke Angelo Bronzino, Strassburg, 1911, p. 14; McComb, Agnolo Bronzino, His Life and Works, Cambridge, 1928, p. 133; Harck, Quadri di Maestri Italiani in Possesso di Privati a Berlino, Arch. Stor. dell' Arte, I (1889), 205; Museum News, No. 21, April 1914, repr.; Connoisseur, LXXXIV (Nov. 1929), 279.

GIOVANNI BATTISTA TIEPOLO 1696-1770

DESCENDANT of a Venetian merchant family, Tiepolo early arrived at mastery of the painter's art, enriched his own city with a vast number of his works, painted for three years in Würzburg, was one of the founders and first president of the Venetian Academy, went to Madrid in 1762, where he remained to the end of his life. Heir of Titian, Tintoretto, Veronese, the legacy of joy and richness of the last named artist was his chief dower. Last of the great decorators, less powerful than his precursors, amazing virtuosity gives his work light grace, radiant charm.

HEAD OF AN OLD MAN

Rendered with rapid, fluid brush, with more strength than his usual ceiling decorations, here in portrait study he gives better account of his technical abilities than in many more ambitious compositions. Realistic, impressionistic, textures of aged skin, of beard, of fabrics, are admirably recorded.

Oil on canvas, 16 x 18⅝ in. (41 x 47 cm.) Unsigned.
Gift of Edward Drummond Libbey, 1925.

COLLECTION: Edward Drummond Libbey, 1925.

EXHIBITION: Chicago, Art Institute, Paintings, Drawings and Prints by the Two Tiepolos, 1938, No. 17.

18

GIOVANNI ANTONIO GUARDI 1698-1760

SON OF the painter Domenico Guardi and elder brother of the more famous Francesco Guardi, a founder of the Venetian Academy, few paintings surely by his hand are now known. Deriving from Sebastiano Ricci and Tiepolo, he combined their styles felicitously.

THE HOLY FAMILY

Strongly pyramidal in composition, rich in color, cool notes on the left balance warm yellows in the garment of the angel on the right. Ascending lines dominate in the attitude of the Virgin presenting the Child to God the Father, and in the upraised arms of an angel. Strong cloud effect forms dramatic background to closely massed figures.

Oil on canvas, $37\frac{7}{8}$ x $45\frac{1}{2}$ in. (96 x 116 cm.) Unsigned.
Gift of Edward Drummond Libbey, 1925.

COLLECTIONS: Barozzi, Venice; Edward Drummond Libbey, 1925.

EXHIBITIONS: Florence, Italy, Pitti Palace, 1922; St. Louis, City Art Museum, Eighteenth Century Venetian Painting, 1936, No. 15; Iowa City, Iowa, State University, Figure Paintings, 1936, No. 27; Springfield, Mass., Museum of Fine Arts, Guardi Exhibition, 1937; Kansas City, William Rockhill Nelson Gallery of Art, Anniversary Exhibition of Venetian Paintings and Drawings of the Eighteenth Century, 1937.

REFERENCES: Ojetti, Dami and Tarchiani, La Pittura Italiana del Seicento e del Settecento alla mostra di Palazzo Pitti, Florence, 1922, p. 157, repr.; Fiocco, Francesco Guardi, Florence, 1923, p. 69, No. 39, Pl. 29, repr., (attr. to Francesco Guardi); Lasareff, Francesco and Gianantonio Guardi, Burlington Magazine, LXV (Aug. 1934), 53-72; Bulletin, City Art Museum, St. Louis, XXI (March 1936), 26, No. 15, 40, repr.

SPANISH PAINTINGS

Jusepe de Ribera	Portrait of a Musician
Francisco de Zurbaran	The Flight into Egypt
Diego Rodriguez de Silva y Velasquez	Man with a Wine Glass
Francisco Jose de Goya y Lucientes	A Bull Fight
Hermengildo Anglada-Camarasa	On the Sofa
Joseph Mompou	The Shore
Mariano Andreu	Bastinadoes

JUSEPE DE RIBERA 1590-1652

FORMED by the teaching of Ribalta, and enthusiasm for Raphael, Caravaggio, Correggio, in religious and mythological pictures Ribera reflects their styles; in portraiture he is himself. Spanish by birth and early training, he studied further in Rome, spent most of his life in Naples, then a Spanish dependency. His works range from sweet sentimentality to rugged realism; his handling of light frequently shows overemphasis upon contrast.

PORTRAIT OF A MUSICIAN

One of the finest of his portraits, memorable in its simplicity, it is worthy of inclusion among his masterpieces. Almost in monochrome, it depends for its effect upon contrast of brilliantly lighted face, hand and sheet of music, with adjacent rich black of hair, beard and garment against background ranging from grey almost to black. Somber in lack of enlivening color, it is dramatic, impressive in illumined features and quiet thoughtful eyes.

Oil on canvas, $24\frac{5}{8}$ x $30\frac{3}{8}$ in. (63 x 77 cm.) Signed at right near center: Jusepe de Ribera f 1638.
Gift of Edward Drummond Libbey, 1925.

COLLECTIONS: Gift to Potocki family from King Augustus III of Poland; G. Stroganoff, Rome; Edward Drummond Libbey, 1925.

EXHIBITIONS: New York, Metropolitan Museum of Art, Spanish Paintings, 1928, No. 54, repr. in catalogue; San Diego Museum of Fine Arts, Spanish Paintings, 1930; Brooklyn Museum, Spanish Art, 1935, No. 52; Toledo Museum, Portraits and Portraiture Throughout the Ages, 1937, No. 11.

REFERENCES: Mayer, Ribera, Leipzig, 1908 and 1923, p. 127-128, Pl. 35, repr.; Pièces de choix de la collection du Comte Grégoire Stroganoff, Rome, 1912, II, 107, repr. Pl. LXXXII; Allgemeines Künstler-Lexikon, Leipzig, 1934, XXVIII, 233; L'Arte, 1909, p. 79; Museum News, No. 48, March 1926, repr.

FRANCISCO DE ZURBARAN   1598-1662

MOST SPANISH of the Spanish artists, for he alone of the great ones never travelled or studied abroad, Zurbaran was born near Seville, studied there with an unimportant painter of images. Much of his work was done in Seville, some in Madrid, where, probably on Velasquez' nomination, he was made Painter to the King, and where he passed the last years of his life. Painting always from the model and from actual costume, his work is realistic, truthful. His compositions, sometimes formal, static, do not lack in invention, natural incident.

THE FLIGHT INTO EGYPT

Composition carefully planned, the many rigid figures confer dignity, sustain interest. Sequences of line, color, value, carry across the canvas, the brighter, but not over-intense colors marking the principal figures. Rich, brilliant colors contrast with dark, quiet tones. Sentiment of departure is unforced, amply indicated. Quality of the painting ranks it among the best of his works outside of Spain, on a par with those remaining there.

Oil on canvas, $97\frac{5}{8}$ x $75\frac{5}{8}$ in. (249 x 192 cm.) Unsigned.
Gift of Edward Drummond Libbey, 1923.

COLLECTIONS: Fourth Earl of Clarendon, British Ambassador at Madrid, 1833-39; Sixth Earl of Clarendon, London (sold 1920).

EXHIBITIONS: New York, Metropolitan Museum of Art, Spanish Paintings, 1928, No. 66, repr. in catalogue; San Diego, Museum of Fine Arts, Spanish Paintings, 1930; Philadelphia, Pennsylvania Museum, Masters of Spanish Paintings, 1937.

REFERENCES: Waagen, Treasures of Art in Great Britain, London, 1854, II, 458; Tietze, Meisterwerke Europäische Malerei in Amerika, Vienna, 1935, p. 18, repr., p. 324; Museum News, No. 46, March 1924, repr.; Art News, XXXV (April 17, 1937), 10, repr.; Literary Digest, CXXIII (May 22, 1937), 25, repr.; Life, IV (May 16, 1938), repr. in color.

DIEGO RODRIGUEZ DE SILVA Y VELASQUEZ 1599-1660

SEVILLIAN, pupil of masters whose names live chiefly through their illustrious student, painter to King Philip IV, valet of the royal chamber, created a knight of Calatrava, decorated with the Order of Santiago, Velasquez was honored by his contemporaries as by posterity. Godfather to the French Impressionists as Greco was to the Post-Impressionists, he has been called the greatest of painters. One might say without Velasquez, no Manet; without Manet, no modern painting. Raphael did not please him. Titian, Rubens, Greco influenced him; he himself influenced legions. Endowed with sure vision, accurate observation, a perfect sense of form and color, favored with a life serene and dignified, a mature and serious student, he maintained a uniformly high standard. Greco reaches supreme heights; he also falls to low levels. Velasquez, more thoughtful, less emotional, holds more constantly to a lofty plane.

MAN WITH A WINE GLASS

Definite in composition, postive in drawing, the figure beautifully placed on the canvas, features sharp, outline firm, the Man with a Wine Glass ranks as one of the great works of Velasquez. Color of face, deepened, intensified, is carried across yellow background tinged with green into red-amber wine. Rich black of costume is strong contrast to white collar. Marvelous painting of the glove can be compared only with Hals and Rembrandt, his Dutch contemporaries. Free and original technical execution are marked especially in glove and collar. Bold, impressive, reserved yet scintillant, it shows the mastery of great genius. It was probably painted about 1623, soon after Velasquez arrived in Madrid. A variant exists in the Rouen Geographer, painted earlier, repainted later than this picture.

Oil on canvas, 30 x 25 in. (76 x 63 cm.) Unsigned.
Gift of Edward Drummond Libbey, 1925.

COLLECTIONS: G. Prior Goldney, Bart., Derriads, Chippenham, Wilts; Edward Drummond Libbey, 1915-1925.

EXHIBITIONS: Bristol, England, Fine Arts Academy, 1893; Bristol, England, Fine Arts Academy, 1906; Cambridge, Mass., Fogg Museum, 1914; Cleveland Museum, Inaugural, 1916, No. 24, catalogue p. 384, repr.; New York, Reinhardt Galleries, 1924; New York, Metropolitan Museum, Spanish Paintings, 1928, No. 58, repr. in catalogue; Chicago, Art Institute, Century of Progress, 1933, No. 184,

DIEGO RODRIGUEZ DE SILVA Y VELASQUEZ 1599-1660

repr. in catalogue, Pl. XXX; Cleveland Museum, Twentieth Anniversary, 1936, No. 251, repr. in catalogue, Pl. XLIX; Baltimore Museum of Art, Spanish Paintings, 1937, No. 10, repr. in catalogue; Toledo Museum, Portraits and Portraiture Throughout the Ages, 1937, No. 13.

REFERENCES: Mayer, Velasquez, Berlin, 1924, p. 74; Mayer, Velasquez, London, 1936, p. 104: Roos, An Illustrated Handbook of Art History, New York, 1937, p. 172, repr.; Mayer, The Man with the Wine Glass by Diego Velasquez, Art in America, III (June 1915), 183-187, repr.; Museum News, No. 48, March 1926, repr.; American Magazine of Art, XIX (April 1928); Cortissoz, Paintings by Velasquez in America, International Studio, LXXXVII (June 1928), 35-47, repr.; Country Life, LIV (June 1928), 34, repr. in color; Bulletin, Art Institute of Chicago, Apr.-May 1933, repr. on cover; Art News, XXXI (May 27, 1933), 17; Fine Arts, XX (June 1933), 17; Pantheon, XII (Dec. 1933), 380, repr.; Town and Country, June 15, 1933, repr.; Children's Museum News, No. 8, Sept. 1935, repr.; Fortune, XVII (Jan. 1938), 74, repr. in color.

FRANCISCO JOSE DE GOYA Y LUCIENTES   1746-1828

CLAIMING nature, Velasquez and Rembrandt as his masters, Goya emerged unheralded from the nebulous mediocrity that had been Spanish art since Velasquez, a luminary of the first magnitude. Variable star, his art as uneven as his life erratic, he essayed diverse subjects in many media in original, independent style. He had amazing technical facility, splendid feeling for composition and harmony of color. His range is broad. Village and country scenes are idyllic, charming as Watteau or Fragonard. Portraits are strong, realistic, searching, characterful, whether of young and delightful children, or of faded, decadent adults, disagreeable in their ugliness. His etchings are caustic, satiric invective against the abuses and depravities of his time. His scenes from the struggle against the French invaders are powerful, moving, vigorous record and denunciation.

A BULL FIGHT

Yellows, reds, red-violets skilfully combined with blue-greens and blues mingle and weave through the composition, encompassing the whole range of the value scale, focusing attention on bull, horses, men with a flood of vibrant light. His bold color, free sweep of brushwork are attuned to masterful depiction of the Spanish national sport. Spontaneity, vigor, strength dominate the canvas, the unpleasant features of the scene far subordinated to beauty of color, richness of composition. Stylistic analogies to other paintings by Goya indicate a date near 1810. Similarities of subject and handling appear in his etchings of bull fights, published in 1815. He used the principal figures of the composition in the lithograph Bravo Toro of 1825.

Oil on canvas, $36\frac{3}{4}$ x $25\frac{1}{8}$ in. (93 x 64 cm.) Unsigned.
Gift of Edward Drummond Libbey, 1929.

COLLECTIONS: M. Edwards, Paris, (sold May 25, 1905); M. Xanroff, Paris.

EXHIBITION: San Francisco, California Palace of the Legion of Honor, Goya Paintings, 1937, No. 26, repr. in catalogue, p. 32.

REFERENCES: Tietze, Meisterwerke Europäische Malerei in Amerika, Vienna, 1935, p. 324, repr. p. 24; Art Digest, IV (Nov. 1, 1929), 11, repr.; Art News, XXVIII (Nov. 2, 1929), 3, repr.; Museum News, No. 55, Dec. 1929, repr.; Parnassus, V (Feb. 1933), 11, repr.

HERMENGILDO ANGLADA-CAMARASA   1871-

PRODUCT of Parisian training in addition to that of his native Barcelona, Anglada developed a style personal yet Spanish. Primarily a figure painter, preferring the types of his own people, subject even more than technique gives the national character to his work. Colorful costume, heavy impasto, planned relation of areas of light and color confer dazzling brilliance upon much of his work.

ON THE SOFA

High in key, striking in vivid decorative quality of its composition, dark hair and eyes are the only contrast in a tonal scheme of light upon dark. Unusual conception is sustained by technique of related values of contrasting colors applied with vigorous brush stroke.

Oil on canvas, 41 x 75 in. (104 x 191 cm.) Signed in lower right corner: H. Anglada-Camarasa.
Acquired 1931.

EXHIBITIONS: Liverpool, Walker Art Gallery, 58th Autumn Exhibition, 1930; Cleveland Museum, Foreign Section of 1930 Carnegie International, 1931; Chicago, Art Institute, Foreign Section of 1930 Carnegie International, 1931; Providence, R. I., Rhode Island School of Design, Modern Spanish Paintings, 1934, No. 2.

REFERENCE: London Studio, XVI (Jan. 15, 1926), repr. in color.

JOSEPH MOMPOU   1888-

BORN AT Barcelona, he has recently come into prominence through his gay and brilliant landscapes. Usually working in high key, he secures suggestive representation with slightest apparent effort.

THE SHORE

Cool, clear water contrasting with hot sands of the seashore, bright color, brilliant sunlight suggest Mediterranean coast. Softly modelled hills form pleasing background to beach and sea; casually sketched rectangular buildings take their ordered places in the composition.

Oil on canvas, 32 x $25\frac{7}{8}$ in. (81 x 66 cm.) Signed at lower right: Mompou; on back of canvas, J. Mompou 1932.
Acquired 1934.

EXHIBITIONS: Pittsburgh, Pa., Carnegie Institute, 1933 International, No. 307; Cleveland Museum, Foreign Section of 1933 Carnegie International, 1934; Toledo Museum, Foreign Section of 1933 Carnegie International, 1934, No. 206.

MARIANO ANDREU 1888-

NATIVE of Barcelona, Andreu's work shows in use of form as design the influence of his fellow-townsman Picasso, imposed upon his English training. From these and other sources springs the spontaneous individual style evident in gracefully composed still lifes and figure subjects, the lyric charm and rhythmic line of his compositions.

BASTINADOES

Perhaps reminiscent of his designs for the theatre, this painting is suggestive of stage setting. Architecture and trees, in flat, thin rendering, serve as foil to prominent central figures. Subtle interplay of diagonal structure, rhythmic line and color unify and balance the composition.

Oil on mahogany, $22\frac{1}{8}$ x $17\frac{3}{8}$ in. (56 x 44 cm.) Signed in lower left corner: Mariano Andreu Juillet 34.
Acquired 1936.

EXHIBITIONS: Pittsburgh, Pa., Carnegie Institute, 1935 International, No. 328; Cleveland Museum, Foreign Section of 1935 Carnegie International, 1936; Toledo Museum, Foreign Section of 1935 Carnegie International, 1936, No. 241.

REFERENCE: Museum News, No. 77, Dec. 1936.

GERMAN PAINTINGS

Albrecht Durer	The Wife of Jobst Planckfelt
Lucas Cranach	Martin Luther and his Friends
Hans Holbein the Younger	Catherine Howard
Barthel Bruyn the Younger	Father and Sons
Barthel Bruyn the Younger	Mother and Daughters
Adolphe Schreyer	The Standard Bearer
Adolphe Schreyer	The Wallachian Team
Franz von Stuck	The Artist's Daughter
Carl Hofer	Flower Girl
Max Pechstein	Still Life with Calla Lilies

41

ALBRECHT DÜRER 1471-1528

PROFOUND thinker, greatest artist of Germany, his efforts directed by the exigencies of time and place largely to engraving on wood and copper, Dürer's genius is best known through his widely distributed engravings. Born at Nuremberg, godson of Koburger, intimate of Erasmus, Luther, Pirkheimer, Melancthon, in Italy he visited Bellini and Mantegna, in Flanders was honored by Massys, Mabuse, Van Orley, Patinir. Three early influences combined in the formation of his artistic style; from Wolgemut came foundation and the Nuremberg tradition, from Schongauer the Rhenish style of the fifteenth century, and from Mantegna that of Italy in the quattrocento. Though but fair colorist, Dürer is supreme as designer and draughtsman. Keen observer, accurate recorder, serious-minded, as intellectual artist he stands with Leonardo and Michelangelo.

THE WIFE OF JOBST PLANCKFELT

Firm draughtsmanship, sensitive, delicate delineation at once model the figure, express character, quality. White headdress, dark garment, warm flesh tones are enhanced by brilliant light green-blue background. The picture bespeaks refinement, style, intelligence of the artist, in crisply defined linear pattern; fine consideration for relationship of shapes and spaces suggest his achievements in engraving. Mentioned in his diary of his trip to the Netherlands is a portrait of the wife of his landlord at Antwerp, painted in 1521. This is presumably that portrait.

Oil on oak, $10\frac{1}{2}$ x $12\frac{1}{2}$ in. (27 x 32 cm.) Unsigned.
Gift of Edward Drummond Libbey, 1936.

COLLECTION: Prince Radziwill, Poland.

EXHIBITION: Toledo Museum, Portraits and Portraiture Throughout the Ages, 1937, No. 2.

REFERENCES: Conway, Literary Remains of Albrecht Dürer, London, 1889, p. 119; Waetzoldt, Dürer und Seine Zeit, Vienna, 1935, p. 184; Tietze and Tietze-Conrat, Der Reife Dürer, Basel and Leipzig, 1938, II, 19-20, No. 793, repr. p. 159; Art News, XXXIV (Feb. 29, 1936), 5, repr.; Art Digest, X (March 1, 1936), 14, repr.; Die Weltkunst, Berlin, March 1936 repr.; Parnassus, VIII (March 1936), 20, repr.; American Magazine of Art, XXIX (April 1936), 250-1, repr.; American German Review, June 1936, repr. frontispiece; Museum News, No. 81, March 1938, repr.

SON AND father of painters, born into the School of Franconia, later settling at Wittenberg, where Luther nailed his theses to the church door, there he founded, under the patronage of the Elector, the School of Saxony. Probably pupil of his father, he was influenced by Altdorfer, travelled in Austria, in the Netherlands, where twelve years before Dürer he met Massys and Mabuse, borrowed from both for the execution of the triptych of the Family of the Virgin now at Frankfort. Charged by the Elector of Saxony about 1510 with the production of sixty portraits, his atelier became a factory, his signature a trade-mark. His name on a painting stands for a dynasty rather than an individual. Painter of the Reformation, friend of Luther and its other leaders, therefore popular, his color is harsh, his drawing hard, his design weak; but his quaint, naive concepts, especially of his nudes, impart interest and charm to his work.

MARTIN LUTHER AND HIS FRIENDS

Surrounding their protector, Elector John Frederick the Magnanimous, stand Luther, Zwingli, Melancthon, Oecolampadius and others. Dark tones of robes and background are relieved by the faces, the heavy chain, rich embroidery and white shirt of the central figure. The others, crowded, lacking focal point, seem accessories to the Elector, dominant by bulk and position. Faithful, meticulous portraiture, sharp in line, firm in contour, gives evidence of the finer qualities of the school. In upper right a light landscape passage, in lower left an unexplained cherub, perhaps added later, enliven the composition.

Oil on wood, $15\frac{3}{4}$ x $27\frac{7}{8}$ in. (40 x 71 cm.) Unsigned.
Gift of Edward Drummond Libbey, 1925.

COLLECTIONS: Rt. Hon. Cornelia, Countess of Craven, Coombe Abbey, Coventry; Edward Drummond Libbey, 1925.

EXHIBITIONS: Manchester, England, Art Treasures, 1857, No. 451; Toledo Museum, Portraits and Portraiture Throughout the Ages, 1937, No. 3.

REFERENCES: Waagen, Art Treasures in Great Britain, London, 1854, III, 219; Kuhn, German Paintings in American Collections, Cambridge, 1936, p. 45, No. 150, repr. Pl. XXVII (attr. to follower of Lucas Cranach the Elder).

SUPERB colorist, greatest painter of Germany, as Dürer was her greatest artist, separated from him in age by but twenty-six years, standing with him at the zenith of the German Renaissance, the one marks the beginning of modern times, the other the end of the Gothic age. Born at Augsburg, which he quitted early for Basle, one of the intellectual crossroads of Europe, he painted vigorously there for a decade, designed for the printer Froben, visited Italy and France. Driven by growing Protestant fanaticism, drawn by increasing demand for works of art, Holbein departed Basle for England in 1526, carrying an introduction from Erasmus to Sir Thomas More. Thenceforward, adapting himself to conditions as he found them, he narrowed the wide range of his work to portraiture alone. Like the contemporary Clouets of France he first made studies of his sitters in crayon. His portraits, objective, impartial, reflect infallibly the characters of the subjects. His eye most shrewd, his mind most just, his hand most true, he remains supreme portraitist of all times.

CATHERINE HOWARD

The inscription "Etatis Suae 21" establishes the date 1540-41 for this representation of Henry VIII's fifth queen. Against deep blue-green background, most complimentary to the auburn hair, quiet, dignified, holding her own counsel, attired in rich and voluminous garment, the figure bespeaks the majesty of England's queen. Simplified, reduced to essentials, faultlessly drawn, beautifully composed, the character observed keenly, recorded faithfully, not interpreted, the painting stands a perfect example of objective portraiture, a high achievement by one of the greatest of masters.

Oil on oak, $20\frac{1}{4}$ x $29\frac{1}{8}$ in. (51 x 74 cm.) Inscribed on background: Etatis Suae 21.
Gift of Edward Drummond Libbey, 1925.

COLLECTIONS: Cromwell Bush, London; James H. Dunn, Canada; Edward Drummond Libbey, 1915-1925.

EXHIBITIONS: New York, Reinhardt Galleries, 1928, No. 3, repr. in catalogue; Chicago, Art Institute, Century of Progress, 1933, No. 19, repr. in catalogue; Toledo Museum, Portraits and Portraiture Throughout the Ages, 1937, No. 7.

REFERENCES: Chamberlain, Hans Holbein the Younger, New York, 1913, II, 194-196, and 348; Gans, Holbein (Klassiker der Kunst), 1921, p. 243, repr. Pl. 126;

Christoffel, Hans Holbein, d. J., Berlin, 1926, p. 118; Stein, Holbein, Berlin, 1929, p. 296; Bulliet, Art Masterpieces of the Fair Exhibited at the Art Institute of Chicago, 1933, No. 4, repr.; Kuhn, German Paintings in American Collections, Cambridge, 1936, p. 83, No. 273, repr. Pl. LXXVIII; Roos, An Illustrated Handbook of Art History, New York, 1937, p. 170, repr.; Cust, Burlington Magazine, XVII (July 1910), 193-199, repr.; The Antiquarian, May 1924, repr.; International Studio, LXXXIV (July 1926), 43, repr.; Vaughn, International Studio, LXXXVIII (Dec. 1927), 65, repr.; Museum News, No. 48, March 1926, repr.; Art Digest, III (March 1,1928), repr.; Art News, XXVI (March 3, 1928), repr.; Literary Digest, March 31, 1928, repr.; Arts and Decoration, XXIV (April 1928), 70, repr.; La Renaissance de l'Art, Paris, April 1928, repr.; Cicerone, XX (1928), 315, repr.; Mayer, Pantheon, II (July 1928), 331, repr. in color; International Studio, XCI (Oct. 1928), repr. in color; Chicago Art Institute Bulletin, April-May 1933, repr.; Connoisseur, XVI (May 1933), 345; Art News, XXXI (May 13, 1933), 10, repr.; American Magazine of Art, XXVI (June 1933), 28, repr.; Parnassus, V (May 1933), 8-11, repr.; Town and Country, June 15, 1933, repr.; Illustrated London News, Nov. 4, 1933, p. 737, repr.

BARTHEL BRUYN THE YOUNGER 1530-1610

PUPIL and follower of a more capable father, heir to his active workshop, among the last of the painters of the Cologne School, he painted chiefly portraits or religious figures with portrait heads. Though fresh, direct, and strongly modelled, lifelike qualities are in slight evidence in his portraits. Sombre colors, making flesh tones bloodless and pale, are combined with delicately softened shadows, and cool arrangements of black, white, silver-grey and blue-green devoid of accent.

FATHER AND SONS

Against dull yellow-green background are posed father and his sons, filling, crowding the panel. Severe countenance, fixed gaze of father is reflected in his children. Forced design, rigid pose, tight drawing strangely confer quaint naivety, unintentional charm on formal Germanic portraiture.

Oil on oak, 17⅝ x 22½ in. (45 x 57 cm.) Unsigned.
Gift of Edward Drummond Libbey, 1925.

COLLECTIONS: Mori, Paris; Rt. Hon. Cornelia, Countess of Craven, Coombe Abbey, Coventry; Edward Drummond Libbey, 1925.

EXHIBITION: Toledo Museum, Portraits and Portraiture Throughout the Ages, 1937, No. 9.

REFERENCES: Kuhn, German Paintings in American Collections, Cambridge, 1936, p. 29, No. 46, repr. Pl. X.

BARTHEL BRUYN THE YOUNGER 1530-1610

MOTHER AND DAUGHTERS

Companion piece to the preceding picture, it shows the same mannerisms of style and composition, the severity softened somewhat by the feminine content, the bland visage of the mother, the sobriety of coloring relieved by the headdresses, chains and jewelled buckles.

Oil on oak, 17¾ x 22½ in. (45 x 57 cm.) Unsigned.
Gift of Edward Drummond Libbey, 1925.

COLLECTIONS: Mori, Paris: Rt. Hon. Cornelia, Countess of Craven, Coombe Abbey, Coventry; Edward Drummond Libbey, 1925.

EXHIBITION: Toledo Museum, Portraits and Portraiture Throughout the Ages, 1937, No. 10.

REFERENCES: Kuhn, German Paintings in American Collections, Cambridge, 1936, p. 29, No. 47, repr. Pl. X.

ADOLPHE SCHREYER

1828-1899

FOLLOWER of Fromentin, who in turn was follower of a phase of Delacroix, Schreyer was born at Frankfort, trained at Düsseldorf and Munich, lived in Paris and travelled in the Near East. The oriental scene of the Byronic period, horses in action or semi-repose, drifting snows or swirling sands are his subjects; colors at once realistic and idyllic coupled with sound German drawing, his means.

THE STANDARD BEARER

Its subject Arab in flowing costume on fine steed, formally posed against background suggestive of his native habitat, the painting relies for its merit upon accurate draughtsmanship, striking color, contrast of lighting, all used for dramatic and romantic effect.

Oil on canvas, 28 x 36⅝ in. (71 x 93 cm.) Signed in lower right corner: Ad. Schreyer.
Gift of Arthur J. Secor, 1922.

COLLECTIONS: Baron de Tuyll, Secretary of Dutch Legation, Washington, to 1906; Arthur J. Secor, 1906-1922.

REFERENCE: Museum News, No. 41, April 1922, repr.

THE WALLACHIAN TEAM

Horses seek protection from the gusty blasts under shelter of a thatched projection from a low building. The painting is almost in monochrome, as befits its subject, the chill and blizzard well suggested.

Oil on canvas, 33⅛ x 19⅝ in. (84 x 50 cm.) Signed in lower right corner: Ad. Schreyer.
Gift of Arthur J. Secor, 1922.

COLLECTION: Arthur J. Secor, 1904-1922.

REFERENCE: Museum News, No. 41, April 1922, repr.

54

FRANZ VON STUCK

1863-1928

REMINISCENT at once of Böcklin and the Pre-Raphaelites, Stuck's works are well modelled, firm in contours, dominated by line. His subjects are usually religious, mythological or fanciful. Illustrator before painter, he developed a fertility of imagination and invention, which, coupled with a sound but narrative style, gave him great popularity in the late nineteenth century.

THE ARTIST'S DAUGHTER

Composition of curving lines within octagonal frame shows strength in linear design and decorative quality. The face seemingly chiselled rather than painted is set within white frills of intense harsh blue bonnet, all against dull background. The hand of the illustrator is evident in the hard line, the cold, calculated approach.

Oil on poplar, $14\frac{1}{4}$ x $14\frac{1}{4}$ in. (36 x 36 cm.) Signed at lower right: Franz von Stuck.
Gift of Edward Drummond Libbey, 1912.

CARL HOFER

Educated in his birthplace, Karlsruhe, Hofer was first influenced by Thoma and Böcklin. For a number of years he worked in Rome; thereafter in Paris. In Germany after 1920 he consolidated the monumental figure painting of his Italian days, the form and color concepts of Cézanne, gleanings from Greco, Delacroix and Hodler, into a vigorous expressionism. Possessing the romantic, seeking the classic, readily adjustable to changing formulae, Hofer holds high position among contemporary painters.

Flower Girl

Bold modelling, vigorous drawing, immobile solidity of form impart a classical and heroic quality to the figure. Strong orange, red-orange, red and purple, greyed white, yellow and green of bouquet provide emphatic color notes. Dull tones of white apron, slaty dress, red trimming accentuate high key of pink sleeves, lusciously painted yellow kerchief. Subdued violets, greyed greens, touches of pale and brilliant blue produce effective background.

Oil on canvas, $32\frac{1}{8}$ x $39\frac{7}{8}$ in. (82 x 101 cm.) Signed in lower left corner: CH 35.

Acquired 1938.

Exhibitions: Pittsburgh, Carnegie Institute, 1937 International, No. 353; Toledo Museum, Contemporary Movements in European Painting, 1938, No. 46.

MAX PECHSTEIN 1881-

PECHSTEIN, born in Swickau, studied in Germany, has travelled and worked there, in Italy, Switzerland and France. Entering upon his career just after the turn of the century, he stands high among the German painters of the reaction to Impressionism, seeks through new methods an emphatically expressive art.

STILL LIFE WITH CALLA LILIES

In bold color, broad technique, sturdy green stems supporting white blossoms and heavy green leaves are set in a grey vase against background of tones ranging from pale violet to deepest blue. Crisp line defines the forms, firm modelling effects rugged strength, plastic solidity. Striking effect is obtained by use of strong contrasts along with close and transitional values.

Oil on canvas, $26\frac{3}{4}$ x $38\frac{1}{4}$ in. (68 x 97 cm.) Signed in lower right corner: M. Pechstein 1931.
Acquired 1934.

EXHIBITIONS: Pittsburgh, Pa., Carnegie Institute, 1933 International, No. 345; Cleveland Museum, Foreign Section of 1933 Carnegie International, 1934; Toledo Museum, Foreign Section of 1933 Carnegie International, 1934, No. 76; Toledo Museum, Contemporary Movements in European Painting, 1938, No. 82.

FLEMISH AND BELGIAN PAINTINGS

UNKNOWN ARTIST	ADORATION OF THE KINGS
UNKNOWN ARTIST	ADORATION OF THE MAGI
JAN GOSSART, CALLED MABUSE	CANON JEAN DE CARONDELET
JOACHIM PATINIR	THE JUDGMENT OF PARIS
JOOS VAN CLEVE	PORTRAIT OF A YOUNG WOMAN
JOOS VAN CLEVE	PORTRAIT OF A YOUNG MAN
UNKNOWN ARTIST	THE MARRIAGE OF HENRY VI
PETER PAUL RUBENS	THE HOLY FAMILY
ANTHONY VAN DYCK	ST. MARTIN SHARING HIS MANTLE
LEON DEVOS	SUSANNA

UNKNOWN ARTIST   About 1440

THE MODEST artists of the low countries in the middle ages and the Renaissance, members of a guild, as were other artisans and tradesmen, rarely signed their pictures. Many northern paintings have been assigned to their authors by comparison with well-documented altarpieces or other works, but a vast number still remain nameless, as scholars have as yet failed to discover analagous works of established authorship.

ADORATION OF THE KINGS

Against gold background sheltered by dilapidated roof, the Holy Family in traditional attitude receives homage of the three kings. Realism combines with naive conventions. Figures rendered in flat color areas show patterned effect of early illumination; rich costumes of kings, minutely and accurately rendered, contrast with simple dignity of garments of Virgin and St. Joseph. Highly individualized faces, stiffly attached to bodies, indicate ability of artist, as does masterly rendition of fabrics and effective use of broad planes. The slight restorations, evident in the reproduction, detract little from the beauty of the panel. Many characteristics of the painting suggest a Germanic rather than Flemish origin.

Oil on wood (transferred to pressed-wood panel, 1937), 28 x 51 in. (71 x 130 cm.) Unsigned.
Gift of Edward Drummond Libbey, 1936.

COLLECTIONS: Count Julius Andrassy, Hungary; Swiss private collection.

REFERENCE: Fischer, A Cologne Master of 1450-60, Pantheon, XVIII (Oct. 1936), 318-22, repr.

UNKNOWN ARTIST   Fifteenth Century

ADORATION OF THE MAGI

With all the freshness and charm of manuscript illumination, exquisite harmonies of clear pure colors ranging from rich yellows to red-violets predomi-
nate, opposed to the cooler green and blue-green notes of the garments and
the landscape background. A strongly angular composition, with figures and
accessories crisply drawn, centers upon the Christ child.

Oil on wood, $9\frac{1}{4}$ x $12\frac{1}{2}$ in. (23 x 31 cm.) Unsigned.
Gift of Edward Drummond Libbey, 1925.

COLLECTION: Edward Drummond Libbey,   -1925.

JAN GOSSART, CALLED MABUSE

MABUSE was born at Maubeuge in Hainault, probably studied at Bruges, entered the Antwerp Guild of St. Luke in 1503. In the service of Philip of Burgundy he accompanied him to Rome, worked at Middelburg together with Jacopo de' Barbari. He followed his patron to Utrecht, upon his death found another in Adolphus, lord of Vere, nephew of Philip, and lived out his life at Middelburg. Perhaps pupil of Memling, certainly brought up in the Flemish tradition, Mabuse was the first to introduce the Italianate manner into the Low Countries. In his more ambitious compositions Italian forms, superimposed on concepts of the Germanic north, clutter and crowd with overemphasis on detail, overornate display of architecture. His portraits, his half-length Virgins, adhering more closely to Flemish instincts, proclaim his abilities, rank him in many instances high in the scale of artistic creation.

CANON JEAN DE CARONDELET

In this, perhaps the earliest known work of Mabuse, painted in 1503, youthful face and hands rise in contrast to dark green brocaded garment, trimmed with brown fur, black cap, against dark blue-green background. Eyes, nostrils, mouth, hands, clarify the portrait by delicate delineation of character. Accent of clean-cut line in softly modelled portrait, position of hands, are characteristic of Mabuse. Refinement is evident in brushwork of hair, crisp line of cap, nice differentiation of textures. Graceful, authoritative, the panel is dignified by low-toned and vital color scheme.

Oil on wood, $11\frac{3}{8}$ x $15\frac{3}{4}$ in. (29 x 40 cm.) Unsigned.
Gift of William E. Levis, 1935.

COLLECTIONS: C. T. D. Crews, London; Leopold Hirsch, London, (sold 1934).

EXHIBITIONS: London, Agnew Galleries, 1924, No. 31; London, Burlington House, Flemish and Belgian Art, 1927, No. 200, repr. in catalogue, Pl. LXXX; Toledo Museum, Flemish Primitives, 1935, No. 14, repr. in catalogue; Toledo Museum, Portraits and Portraiture Throughout the Ages, 1937, No. 2.

REFERENCES: Friedländer, Von Eyck bis Bruegel, Berlin, 1921, p. 190; Conway, The Van Eycks and Their Followers, London, 1921, p. 362; Ségart, Jan Gossart dit Mabuse, Brussels, 1923, p. 114, repr. p. 12; Friedländer, Die Altniederländische Malerei, Berlin, 1924, VIII, 159, No. 51, repr. Pl. XLIII; Catalogue Leopold Hirsch Sale, Christie's, London, May 11, 1934, repr. No. 112; Museum News, No. 74, March 1936, repr.; Art News, XXXIV (April 11, 1936), 14-15, repr.; Illustrated London News, May 2, 1936, p. 777, repr.

JOACHIM PATINIR   1475/80-1524

INSPIRED by Bosch, David, Massys, appreciated by Dürer, Patinir worked
with Massys, Van Cleve, Isenbrant, in whose pictures he sometimes painted
the landscapes. In his works for the first time landscape is dominant, no
longer subordinated as background to figures as an incidental element of
composition. Sometimes called father of landscape painting, his art brought
to larger proportions, independent importance, the broad views casually introduced by his predecessors.

THE JUDGMENT OF PARIS

Thoroughly characteristic is the classically titled group in the foreground,
dwarfed by the immense grandeur of nature. Farm houses, castles, cities enlivening rolling valleys, craggy hills—fantastic landscape of rich, deep tones
in the foreground, stretches through ever-lightening bluish atmosphere, to pale
and vanish in far distance. Quiet pastoral elements give lyric relief to dramatic strength of surroundings.

Oil on walnut, $12\frac{3}{4}$ x $17\frac{1}{8}$ in. (32 x 43 cm.) Unsigned. Seal with unidentified
coat of arms on back.
Acquired 1935.

EXHIBITION: Toledo Museum, Flemish Primitives, 1935, No. 34, repr.
REFERENCE: Art News, XXXIV (Feb. 1, 1936), 7, repr.

JOOS VAN CLEVE

1480/90-1540

PRAISED by Van Mander as brilliant colorist and eminent portraitist, painter of landscape and historical subject as well, Van Cleve holds prominent position in the line of artistic descent from the Van Eycks to Rubens. Long forgotten, his artistic personality has been restored by researches of the last century. Admitted, already a master, to the Guild at Antwerp in 1511, later its dean, he worked for a time at Cologne, may have visited Italy, France, England. Heir to and adherent of the good Flemish tradition, he produced much work of pleasing quality, fine craftsmanship.

PORTRAIT OF A YOUNG WOMAN

Solidly modelled, well characterized, the panel is considered by Conway one of Van Cleve's best portraits. In green bodice with black velvet neckpiece, fur-trimmed red sleeves and typical Flemish white headdress against grey-green background, formally posed, the figure avoids rigidity, achieves composed and reserved dignity. Evidence of the artist's traditional training in realistic rendering, sincere handling, it was probably painted about 1525, when Van Cleve was approaching the height of his power.

Oil on wood, 13⅝ x 16⅞ in. (35 x 43 cm.) Unsigned.
Gift of Edward Drummond Libbey, 1925.

COLLECTION: Earl of Ellenborough, (sold 1914); Edward Drummond Libbey, 1925.

EXHIBITION: Toledo Museum, Portraits and Portraiture Throughout the Ages, 1937, No. 5.

REFERENCES: Conway, The Van Eycks and Their Followers, London, 1921, p. 411; Baldass, Joos van Cleve, Vienna, 1925, part 1, p. 27, part 2, p. 26, repr. Pl. 57-58; Catalogue, Earl of Ellenborough Collection Sale, Christie's, London, April 3, 1914, No. 107.

72

JOOS VAN CLEVE   1480/90-1540

Portrait of a Young Man

Pendant to preceding picture, similar in execution and tonality, it is presumed to represent one Mynheer Hanneman. Immature, unformed countenance stands out against dark grey-green background, black cap and coat, brown fur collar. Level gaze indicates character ranging from quiet reserve to cold calculation. A coat of arms, as yet unidentified, is painted on the back of the panel. A copy of the portrait, without hands, is in the Johnson Collection, Philadelphia.

Oil on oak, 13½ x 16⅞ in. (34 x 43 cm.) Unsigned. Label on back: Mynheer Hanneman by Joost van Cleef.
Gift of Edward Drummond Libbey, 1925.

COLLECTIONS: Earl of Ellenborough, (sold 1914); Edward Drummond Libbey, 1925.

EXHIBITION: Toledo Museum, Portraits and Portraiture Throughout the Ages, 1937, No. 6.

REFERENCES: Conway, The Van Eycks and Their Followers, London, 1921, p. 411-412; Baldass, Joos van Cleve, Vienna, 1925, part 1, p. 27, part 2, p. 26, repr. Pl. 57-58; Catalogue, Earl of Ellenborough Collection Sale, Christie's, London, April 3, 1914, No. 106.

UNKNOWN ARTIST   About 1500

THE MARRIAGE OF HENRY VI

Although given this title by Horace Walpole, in whose collection the painting once was, more probably it depicts the marriage of some obscure saint.
Walpole's identification of the personnages present, published in his Anecdotes of Painting, is as questionable as that of the authorship of the panel.
Regardless of attribution, it is among the finest of the works of its period,
whether emanating from the Lowlands or from France. Rich brocades of
the young pair and officiating cleric are relieved by more simple garb of
attendants, all against background of fine architecture and receding landscape.
Vertical line of standing figures is repeated in statues within niches, conferring
dignity, poise, simplicity to the composition. Strong color and value rhythms
weave across the panel, giving variety and lively interest. High and low values
of red-orange melt imperceptibly into the beautiful browns, complemented by
varying tones of green. In its somewhat repainted condition determination of
authorship is most difficult.

Oil on oak, 34 x 37⅜ in. (86 x 95 cm.) Unsigned. Inscription, probably
added in Walpole's time, in upper corners of painting gives names of personnages and subject of scene.
Gift of Edward Drummond Libbey, 1925.

COLLECTIONS: Horace Walpole, Strawberry Hill; Duke of Sutherland; Edward
Drummond Libbey, 1916-1925.

EXHIBITION: London, South Kensington (now Victoria and Albert) Museum,
National Portrait Exhibition, 1866, No. 16.

REFERENCES: Walpole, Anecdotes of Painting in England, Strawberry Hill, 1762, I,
32-34, repr. engraving; Dallaway's Edition, 1828, I, 61, repr. p. 34; Catalogue of
the Classic Contents of Strawberry Hill, 1842, No. 25 (Of the twentieth day's sale),
p. 197; S. & E. Harding, Shakespeare Illustrated, London, 1793; Knight, Pictorial
History of England, London, 1837-51; Knight, Pictorial Shakespeare, London,
1839-42; Knight, Old England, London, 1845-46; The Athanaeum, London, April
14, 1866; Nichols, The Builder, May 30, 1866; Notes and Queries, Third Series, X
(July 28, 1866), 61; Woltmann, The Fortnightly Review, Sept. 1866; Museum
News, No. 48, March 1926, repr.; Children's Museum News, No. 10, March 1936,
repr.; Illustrated London News, May 2, 1936, p. 777, repr.

OF MIDDLE-CLASS heritage, pupil of inconsequential and forgotten painters, Rubens became man of the Northern Renaissance, premier artist of his time and place. Courtier, diplomat, scholar, business man as well as painter, his person, his life, his art bespeak the fruits of the earth and the fulness thereof. Succeeding in Italianism, where all his predecessors had failed, he brought the true Renaissance to Flanders. Surpassing all artists of his time in conveying sense of motion and depth, he chose plump, well-developed figures to give short radius, dynamic curves. He kept shadows warm, painted freely with heavy brush strokes. With new vision he contributed a technique of impressionism astounding for its day, a fine harmony of conscious composition. Robust, vigorous, through the quality and mass of his output, through the multitude of his pupils, his influence dominated art for two centuries.

THE HOLY FAMILY

Vibrant with tremendous power, interlacing related curves flow into pattern centering in face and figure of Mary, drawn from that of Hélène Fourment. Form and line are vehicle for luminous tones in unusual arrangement of closely related and delicately contrasting colors. Quiet receding landscape, solid tree trunk and massed branches stabilize the rhythmic and dynamic swirls of composition, the figures instinct with motion. It has been suggested that much of the painting may be the work of Rubens' pupil and assistant, Lucas Franchoys.

Oil on canvas, $62\frac{3}{4}$ x $73\frac{3}{8}$ in. (159 x 186 cm.) Unsigned.
Gift of Arthur J. Secor, 1930.

COLLECTIONS: Comte de Nesselrode, Moscow; P. Mersch, Paris, (sold 1909).

REFERENCES: Catalogue of P. Mersch Collection Sale, Galerie Georges Petit, Paris, May 28, 1909, No. 80, repr. opp. p. 46; Parnassus, II (Jan. 1930), 8; Beaux-Arts, VIII (April 1930), 2, repr.; Art Digest, IV (June 1930), 13, repr.; Art News, XXVIII (June 7, 1930), 14, repr.; International Studio, XCIX (March 1931), repr.; Museum News, No. 62, July 1932, repr. on cover; Children's Museum News, No. 9, Dec. 1935, repr.

ANTHONY VAN DYCK 1599-1641

PRECOCIOUS in the extreme, a master taking pupils at sixteen, chief assistant of Rubens at eighteen, famous at twenty, at forty-two when others begin he had completed a life work. Apprenticeship to Rubens, two trips to Italy, influence of Titian, helped to form his style. Called to England in 1632, he became painter to Charles I, was knighted, produced the many incomparable portraits by which he is better known than by his earlier religious and mythological compositions. Of the multitude of artists deriving from Rubens, Van Dyck alone, a genius versatile, impressionable, inventive, independent, ranks with the immortals.

ST. MARTIN SHARING HIS MANTLE

Finished sketch for an altar-piece in the church at Saventhem and for its later replica in Windsor Castle, the panel was painted about 1622. Thus early the distinguished style of Van Dyck begins to emerge, as in the figure of St. Martin, from the influence of Rubens, still evident in the muscular beggar, and from that of the Venetians, as found in the figures to the Saint's right. Shining armor, brilliant red-orange mantle, white horse, dynamic gesture are prominent against more subdued surrounding tones and lowered value of sky seen through arch. Emphatic line suggests nervous sensitivity; solid piers and arch contribute to stability.

Unveiled in Toledo by Albert I, King of the Belgians, October 7, 1919.
Oil on oak, 19¾ x 25¼ in. (50 x 64 cm.) Unsigned.
Gift of Charles Leon Cardon, 1915.

COLLECTIONS: M. Willebroech, Brussels, (sold 1781); Charles Leon Cardon, Brussels.

EXHIBITION: Brussels, Trésor de l'Art Belge au XVII Siècle, 1910, No. 84, catalogue, p. 62; catalogue de luxe, p. 152, repr. Pl. 59.

REFERENCES: Smith, Catalogue Raisonné, London, 1831, Part III, Van Dyck and Teniers, p. 13; Cust, Anthony van Dyck, London, 1906, p. 32; Godwin, A Van Dyck Saint Martin, Art in America, Feb. 1920, p. 77; Museum News, No. 27, Oct. 1915, repr.; Museum News, No. 34, Nov. 1919, repr.; Museum News, No. 36, May 1920, repr.; Children's Museum News, No. 4, Sept. 1931.

LEON DEVOS

1897-

ENGAGED in the world war from his seventeenth to his twenty-first year, Devos began the study of art in Brussels at the age of twenty-seven. Developing sound structure, firm technique, clear coloring, he soon became prominent among artists of his country, well known abroad.

SUSANNA

Somewhat suggestive of Renoir and Cézanne, the canvas is notable for broad brushwork, solidity of form, clarity of color, surety of drawing. Rich luminosity of flesh, reflected light from white cloth confer dramatic beauty upon the figure.

Oil on canvas, 47 x 58⅞ in. (119 x 150 cm.) Signed in upper left corner: Léon Devos.
Acquired 1936.

EXHIBITIONS: Pittsburgh, Pa., Carnegie Institute, 1935 International, No. 139, repr. in catalogue Pl. 45; Cleveland Museum, Foreign Section of 1935 Carnegie International, 1936; Toledo Museum, Foreign Section of 1935 Carnegie International, 1936, No. 21; Iowa City, Iowa, State University, Figure Paintings, 1936, No. 19.

REFERENCE: Museum News, No. 77, Dec. 1936, repr.

82

DUTCH PAINTINGS

Frans Hals	The Flute Player
Rembrandt van Rijn	Self-Portrait as a Young Man
Ferdinand Bol	The Huntsman
Ferdinand Bol	Girl at Window
Ferdinand Bol	Portrait of a Gentleman
Gerbrand van den Eeckhout	The Magnanimity of Scipio
Nicholas Maes	At the Fountain
Nicholas Maes	Portrait of a Gentleman
Pieter de Hoogh	Interior
Jan van Goyen	Harbor View
Aert van der Neer	Approaching the Bridge
Aert van der Neer	Arrival of the Guest
Jacob van Ruysdael	Landscape
Johannes Hendrick Weissenbruch	The White Cloud
Johannes Hendrick Weissenbruch	Low Tide
Johannes Hendrick Weissenbruch	A Windy Day
Johannes Hendrick Weissenbruch	The Canal
Johannes Hendrick Weissenbruch	Village Scene
Johannes Bosboom	Interior of a Dutch Cathedral
Johannes Bosboom	Church Interior
Josef Israels	Their Daily Bread
Josef Israels	Coming Ashore
Josef Israels	The Parting Day
Josef Israels	Self-Portrait
Josef Israels	The New Flower
Jacob Maris	Scheveningen
Jacob Maris	The Tow Path
Jacob Maris	Boats
Jacob Maris	Amsterdam
Willem Maris	Pasture in Sunshine
Willem Maris	The Lowlands
Anton Mauve	Dutchman Smoking a Pipe
Anton Mauve	Homeward Bound

85

FRANS HALS
1584-1666

HIS BIRTH coincident with Dutch independence, his life encompassing the beginning and end of the great period of Dutch painting, Hals' art was the essence of Dutch life, practical, honest, unimaginative, withal capable, conscientious, independent. His self-satisfied burgher patrons demanded portraits of themselves, alone or in family or civic groups; for his own amusement he painted musicians, street urchins, frequenters of the tavern. Pupil of Karel van Mander, the northern Vasari, he developed his own vigorous, slashing style, brilliantly colorful in his middle period, monochromatic later, always amazing in fidelity, astounding in surety and vitality of draughtsmanship. Among the Dutch inferior in genius only to Rembrandt, his influence was almost as far-reaching.

THE FLUTE PLAYER

Painted about 1630, just as he was reaching the height of his powers and his popularity, the canvas evinces the development of his technique, more rapid in his genre works than in his formal portraits. Large rhythms give dash and movement to swagger head and shoulders; alert face, sensitive hands enliven composition; broad, decisive brush-strokes, bold differentiation of values strengthen and vitalize the canvas. Contours and surfaces are built into substance and form by delicate adjustment of color relation and value, in which respect Hals stands precursor to the Impressionists and their followers. A smaller version is in the collection of Baron de Forest, Paris, formerly in that of Baron de Buernonville and Baroness Hirsch de Gereuth, Paris.

Oil on canvas, $26\frac{1}{8}$ x 26 in. (67 x 66 cm.) Signed at lower right with monogram.
Gift of Edward Drummond Libbey, 1925.

COLLECTIONS: Lady de Clifford, London; E. Warneck, Paris, 1878; Edward Drummond Libbey, 1908-1925.

EXHIBITIONS: New York, Metropolitan Museum, Hudson-Fulton Exhibition, 1909, No. 24, repr. in catalogue; New York, Reinhardt Galleries, 1910; Toledo Museum, Inaugural, 1912, No. 178, catalogue p. 81, repr.; Cleveland Museum, Inaugural, 1916, No. 9, catalogue p. 109, repr.; New York, Reinhardt Galleries, 1928; Detroit Institute of Arts, Hals Exhibition, 1935, No. 14, repr. in catalogue; Toledo Museum, Portraits and Portraiture Throughout the Ages, 1937, No. 12.

FRANS HALS 1584-1666

REFERENCES: Bode, Studien zur Geschichte der holländischen Malerei, Brussels, 1883, No. 59; Moes, Frans Hals, Brussels, 1909, p. 109, No. 222; Hofstede de Groot, Catalogue of Dutch Painters, London, 1910, III, No. 85; Valentiner, Frans Hals, (Klassiker der Kunst, XXVIII), Berlin, 1921, p. 311; Tietze, Meisterwerke Europäischer Malerei in Amerika, Vienna, 1935, No. 161 A, p. 336, repr. p. 161; Valentiner, Frans Hals Paintings in America, Westport, Conn., 1936, No. 56, repr.; Museum News, No. 48, March 1926, repr.; Frankfurter, Paintings by Frans Hals in the United States, Antiquarian, XIII (Sept. 1929), 32-35, repr.; Pantheon, XV (March 1935), 114, repr.; Children's Museum News, No. 12, Sept. 1936, repr.

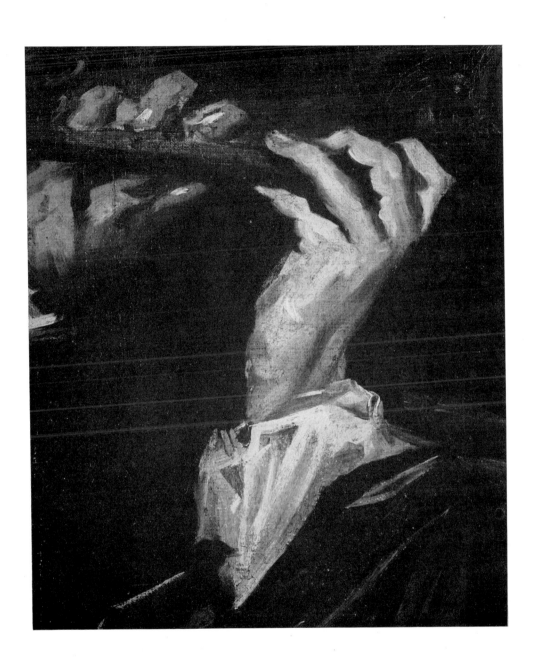

REMBRANDT VAN RIJN   1606-1669

BORN AT Leyden, seat of a great university, turning as a youth from scholarship to art, early removing to Amsterdam, versatile, industrious, prolific, Rembrandt produced about seven hundred paintings, three hundred etchings, two thousands drawings which still remain. He excelled in portraiture, still life, landscape, historical, mythological, and particularly Biblical subjects, figure studies, great portrait compositions. His technique, his genius continued to develop and grow into the last decade of his life. He made light the subject of his pictures and achieved a romantic luminism. Obsessed by chiaroscuro, using a restricted palette, enforcing the simplest means, he painted with light and shade, with most profound and penetrating insight.

SELF-PORTRAIT AS A YOUNG MAN

Pliant young features roundly modelled by light and shade, steady eyes seen through luminous shadow of headdress, picture Rembrandt as a young man, foreshadow, if they do not equal, some of his later triumphs as portraitist. Rich cloak thrown over smooth coat with soft neckband, gold chain and medallion, plumed cap and thick curly hair stand out from subtly glowing grey background. Sequences of broken ovals formed by rhythms of light against dark and dark against light, frame sensitive, pensively thoughtful face, enhance its strong modelling in contrast of values.

Oil on wood, $25\frac{7}{8}$ x $32\frac{1}{4}$ in. (66 x 82 cm.) Signed: RHL 1631.
Gift of Edward Drummond Libbey, 1925.

COLLECTIONS: Stephen Lawley, London (sold March 19, 1906); Edward Drummond Libbey, 1906-1925.

EXHIBITIONS: Leyden, Rembrandt Centennial Celebration, 1905-6, No. 38; New York, Metropolitan Museum, Hudson-Fulton Exhibition, 1909, No. 75, repr. in catalogue; New York, Reinhardt Galleries, 1910, No. 1; Toledo Museum, Inaugural, 1912, No. 200, repr. in catalogue; Cleveland Museum, Inaugural, 1916, No. 16, p. 109, repr. in catalogue; Toledo Museum, Portraits and Portraiture Throughout the Ages, 1937, No. 15.

REFERENCES: Rosenberg, Rembrandt (Klassiker der Kunst), New York, 1909, p. 33, repr.; Hofstede de Groot, Catalogue of Dutch Painters, London, 1916, VI, No. 577; Bredius, The Paintings of Rembrandt, Vienna, 1936, No. 143, repr., Notes, p. 7, (called Young Man with a Plumed Cap); Museum News, No. 48, March 1926.

92

FERDINAND BOL   1616-1680

BORN AT Dordrecht, Bol entered Rembrandt's studio soon after its establishment at Amsterdam. Apt pupil, he so closely followed his master that the work of the two has been frequently confused. Author of a number of group paintings, his more frequent works are single portraits, in which he is at his best. These are studies of light and shade in the Rembrandtesque manner, occasionally approaching the high quality of the master.

THE HUNTSMAN

Reminiscent of Rembrandt, to whom it was once attributed, it is more formal, sharp, dry, than the work of the great master. Blues and oranges, greyed or raised, harmonized by variations of value and intensity, dominate the color scheme. Well-modelled face, carefully painted costume and accessories are set against delicate landscape receding into far distance.

Oil on canvas, $40\frac{5}{8}$ x $50\frac{1}{2}$ in. (103 x 128 cm.) Unsigned.
Gift of Arthur J. Secor, 1926.

COLLECTIONS: Duncan Davidson, Esq., of Tullock, from 1840; Sedelmeyer, Paris, (as Rembrandt).

FERDINAND BOL

GIRL AT WINDOW

More reminiscent of Rembrandt than The Huntsman in effective use of light and shade, head and shoulders stand out brilliantly against depth of interior shadow and dark tones of wall. Meticulous rendering of garment and jewelry, naturalness of pose, warmth and harmony of rich and mellowed coloring, firm draughtsmanship, all give charm and beauty to the canvas.

Oil on canvas, $31\frac{5}{8}$ x $40\frac{5}{8}$ in. (80 x 103 cm.) Signed at lower center: F. Bol 1663.
Gift of Arthur J. Secor, 1928.

COLLECTION: Arthur J. Secor, 1925-1928.

EXHIBITION: Indianapolis, John Herron Art Institute, Dutch Masters of the Seventeenth Century, 1937, No. 7, repr. in catalogue.

REFERENCES: Tietze, Meisterwerke Europäischer Malerei in Amerika, Vienna, 1935, p. 181, repr. p. 337; Museum News, No. 57, June 1930, repr.; Art Digest, IV (Aug. 1930), 15, repr.

FERDINAND BOL   1616-1680

PORTRAIT OF A GENTLEMAN

In outward form deriving from Rembrandt, its values somewhat forced, face
and collar stand forth in luminous glow from dark background, black hat and
cloak merging almost imperceptibly into it. Concentrated light reveals ruddy
flesh tones of carefully drawn, firmly modelled face, proclaiming the artist's
sound technical training, well developed ability.

Oil on oak, $25\frac{7}{8}$ x $33\frac{3}{4}$ in. (66 x 86 cm.) Unsigned.
Gift of Edward Drummond Libbey, 1925.

COLLECTION: Edward Drummond Libbey, 1914-1925.

EXHIBITIONS: Cleveland Museum, Inaugural, 1916, No. 1, p. 107, repr. in catalogue; Toledo Museum, Portraits and Portraiture Throughout the Ages, 1937,
No. 16.

GERBRAND VAN DEN EECKHOUT   1621-1674

BORN AT Amsterdam, entering Rembrandt's studio at age fourteen, he became favorite pupil and later devoted friend of his teacher. Painter and etcher of portraits and historical subjects, at best he approached closely the feeling of his master. Able technician, clever, facile, he readily followed the inspiration of teacher, suggestion of fellow pupil. As Rembrandt's domination waned with passing years he became weak and ineffectual.

THE MAGNANIMITY OF SCIPIO

An elaborate composition, Rembrandt influence is evident in handling of light and shade, Rembrandt technique is approached, notably in head and hands of kneeling figure. Solidity of mass, accuracy of drawing, faithful rendering of stuffs and still life display the artist's capacities. A variant, signed and illegibly dated, is in the New York Historical Society. Another version of the same subject, attributed to Aert de Gelder, exists.

Oil on canvas, $67\frac{1}{2}$ x $54\frac{3}{8}$ in. (171 x 138 cm.) Signed at lower edge towards right: G. V. Eeckhout f. Ad 1658.
Gift of Arthur J. Secor, 1923.

REFERENCE: New York Historical Society Quarterly Bulletin, XI (July 1927), 38-39, repr.

NICHOLAS MAES

NATIVE of Dordrecht, Maes learned to draw there, to paint in Rembrandt's studio. His early work in genre and still life was gradually superseded by more remunerative portraiture. His later style, strongly divergent from the earlier, is noted for its charm of color, its even and diffused lighting, distracting affectation and convention.

AT THE FOUNTAIN

Sheen of satin, softness of fur, translucence of flesh tones, sparkle of jewels contrast with dark rich background, show facility of craftsmanship, adequacy of rendition, which with reputed veracity of representation assured his popularity as portraitist. Rigid, formal pose betrays lack of invention.

Oil on canvas, $34\frac{1}{4}$ x $45\frac{1}{2}$ in. (87 x 115 cm.) Signed in lower left corner: N. Maes 1670.

Gift of Arthur J. Secor, 1924.

NICHOLAS MAES   1632-1693

PORTRAIT OF A GENTLEMAN

Elaborate coiffure and costume of sumptuous velvet, rich brocade, heavy lace
depict styles of the time, confer jewelled opulence upon the figure ostenta-
tiously posed against dark background. Face and hands are rendered in crisp,
firm modelling, more pronounced through contrast with ornate costume.
Oil on canvas, 19⅜ x 15 in. (49 x 38 cm.) Unsigned.
Gift of Edward Drummond Libbey, 1925.

COLLECTIONS: Stroganoff, Rome; Edward Drummond Libbey, 1925.

EXHIBITIONS: College Art Association Circuit, Oct. 1931 to Sept. 1932; Toledo
Museum, Portraits and Portraiture Throughout the Ages, 1937, No. 17.

REFERENCE: Pièces de choix de la collection du Comte Grégoire Stroganoff, Rome,
1912, II, 86, repr. Pl. LXVII.

PIETER DE HOOGH 1629-1683

FORMING with the illustrious Vermeer the stylist school of Delft, De Hoogh, born in Rotterdam, spent his most productive years in Delft, his decline in Amsterdam. Composing always on a few simple themes, he was intrigued by contrast of brilliant against softer light. Domestic scenes of middle-class life mark his best works, giving place in later years to more formal, elegant, cold subjects. Masterly treatment of tone, perspective, atmosphere, combined with admirable figure painting rank him high among all artists of the Netherlands.

INTERIOR

Direct study of interior, furnishings, figures, and particularly light, reminiscent of Vermeer in tonal gradations of wall illumined by windows high on the left, the view extends through the doors of a darker room to the open air. Sequences of values admirably placed lend atmosphere, emphasize accurate perspective. Warm suffusing color invites the eye, confers charm and cheer upon homely scene. A replica of the Bedroom in the Widener collection, both are variants of the similar picture at Karlsruhe.

Oil on canvas, $20\frac{5}{8}$ x $23\frac{7}{8}$ in. (52 x 61 cm.) Signed in lower right corner: P D Hoog.
Gift of Edward Drummond Libbey, 1925.

COLLECTION: Edward Drummond Libbey, 1913-1925.

REFERENCE: Children's Museum News, No. 6, Sept. 1934, repr.

JAN VAN GOYEN 1596-1656

LEYDEN born, set to study art at an early age, pupil of several masters, Van Goyen travelled in France, worked in Haarlem, in Leyden, then settled in The Hague, practiced there his art, engaged in business and ruinous speculation. Dreamer, artist, nervous and impatient genius, his role was the initiation into Dutch art of the individualized landscape, the portraiture of the countryside, later a fetish with artists of Holland. Precursor of Ruysdael and Hobbema, through transparency of color he becomes a luminist.

HARBOR VIEW

Typical in preponderance of sky, reflections in water, dominantly warm greyed color, the canvas is suffused by luminous tone. Monotony is avoided by variety of form, accents of interest in the landscape, rich grouping of clouds. Receding planes of the foreground lead to the central mass of the cathedral, their horizontal lines relieved by the curving forms of the clouds.

Oil on oak, $39\frac{1}{4}$ x $26\frac{7}{8}$ in. (100 x 68 cm.) Unsigned.
Gift of Arthur J. Secor, 1933.

COLLECTION: Arthur J. Secor, 1924-1933.

REFERENCE: Children's Museum News, No. 14, June 1937, repr.

AERT VAN DER NEER

BORN AT Amsterdam, through casual study he turned from business to art. Influenced by Camphuysen and Van de Velde, drawing his subjects chiefly from the neighborhood of Amsterdam, he favored twilight and evening. Dexterity in use of light, poetic conception, romantic subject give his uneven production interest, raise some of it to high level among Dutch landscape.

APPROACHING THE BRIDGE

Cloud forms, in decorative mass, balance and relieve darker tones of linear foreground, composition and value emphasizing diagonal structure. Related color in low-keyed tones of yellow and green concentrate interest on space relations and subject matter, enlivened by diminutive figures in the foreground, cart and occupants, horse and rider.

Oil on oak, oval, $21\frac{1}{8}$ x $15\frac{1}{2}$ in. (54 x 39 cm.) Unsigned.
Gift of Arthur J. Secor, 1933.

COLLECTION: Arthur J. Secor, 1926-1933.

ARRIVAL OF THE GUEST

Flat terrain and overcast sky are dominated by the great tree, its gnarled branches in strong contrast with simple vertical lines of the country mansion. White and brown horses, richly costumed figures add interest to the foreground.

Oil on oak, $21\frac{7}{8}$ x $15\frac{7}{8}$ in. (55 x 40 cm.) Unsigned.
Gift of Arthur J. Secor, 1933.

COLLECTION: Arthur J. Secor, 1926-1933.

JACOB VAN RUYSDAEL   1629-1682

PREEMINENT landscapist of Holland, he developed picturesque, poetic scene into majestic, dignified, monumental landscape. Concentrating on the one field, neglecting all others, his prolific output was uniformly skillful and competent. His chief influences were Van Goyen and, later, Everdingen. Following the latter he painted the grandeur of mountain and waterfall. Composing carefully, assembling, rearranging the elements of nature, balancing its masses in effects of simplicity and grandness, infusing variety and interest into the sky, he depicted the permanent, not the transient aspects of nature.

LANDSCAPE

Imaginative creation rather then copy from nature, the principal areas carefully balanced, the strong horizontal feeling counteracted by the vertical pine trees, the landscape is surmounted by a serenely active sky. Characteristic sombre tones of neutralized deep green are lightened by touches of more brilliant color in the figures, the thatched roof, the sky. Romantic interest is achieved by the introduction of cottage, sailboat, waterfall and distant castle in the rugged setting. The figures were painted by Wouwerman as was frequent in Ruysdael's canvases.

Oil on canvas, 58⅛ x 45¼ in. (147 x 115 cm.) Signed in lower right corner: Ruisdael.

Gift of Arthur J. Secor, 1930.

COLLECTIONS: Vernon Harcourt, 1857; Lewis Harcourt; Edward Dent.

EXHIBITION: London, Royal Academy, Winter Exhibition, 1887, No. 34 (?).

REFERENCES: Waagen, Art Treasures in Great Britain, London, 1854, Supplement, p. 350; Hofstede de Groot, Catalogue of Dutch Painters, London, 1912, IV, No. 267b; Art News, XXIX (Feb. 21, 1931), 8, repr.

JOHANNES HENDRICK WEISSENBRUCH   1824-1903

IN COMPANY with Bosboom precursor of and transitional to The Hague
school of the later nineteenth century, Weissenbruch was enamoured of soft
Holland light, subtly neutralized colors. As a student drawing with accuracy
and detail, brought up in the old school, he helped form the new through
interest in atmospheric effect, absorbing advanced concepts from younger men.

THE WHITE CLOUD

Sky more prominent than land, majestic cloud forms attract and hold interest,
as towpath, canal, and other elements of landscape compose to emphasize their
importance. Activity of line in sky contrasts with static repose on earth;
luminosity of clouds with greyed tones of land and water.

Oil on canvas, 18 x 24$\frac{1}{4}$ in. (46 x 61 cm.) Signed in lower left corner: J. H.
Weissenbruch, 1901.
Gift of Edward Drummond Libbey, 1925.

COLLECTION: Edward Drummond Libbey,   -1925.

114

JOHANNES HENDRICK WEISSENBRUCH 1824-1903

Low Tide

Firm construction, planned composition are enveloped in dull atmosphere. Quiet sky, simple lines of earth and boats, neutralized color produce effect of repose approaching somnolence. Triangles of sails, figures in foreground offer mild relief from monotony of flat beach, uniformly overcast sky.

Oil on canvas, 24 x 31¾ in. (61 x 81 cm.) Signed at lower right corner: J. H. Weissenbruch.
Gift of Arthur J. Secor, 1922.

COLLECTION: Arthur J. Secor, 1914-1922.

REFERENCE: Museum News, No. 41, April 1922, repr.

A Windy Day

Leaden, wind-driven clouds, bending trees and marsh grass give effect of motion, while quiet water mirrors boats and shore. Solid thatched cottage forms a barrier at the left, while receding trees make transition to long horizontal lines of earth and sky at right. Light blue-green and dull red-orange introduced in the cottage enliven greyed color scheme of the painting.

Oil on canvas, 33⅜ x 19⅝ in. (85 x 47 cm.) Signed at lower right corner: J. H. Weissenbruch f.
Gift of Edward Drummond Libbey, 1925.

COLLECTION: Edward Drummond Libbey, -1925.

JOHANNES HENDRICK WEISSENBRUCH   1824-1903

THE CANAL

Typically Dutch in subject matter and flatness of landscape, it displays the
greyed tonalities characteristic of Weissenbruch, the attempt to depict the
peculiar light of Holland.

Watercolor on paper, $10\frac{3}{4}$ x $15\frac{1}{4}$ in. (27 x 39 cm.) Signed in lower left corner:
J. H. Weissenbruch.
Gift of Edward Drummond Libbey, 1925.

COLLECTION: Edward Drummond Libbey,   -1925.

JOHANNES HENDRICK WEISSENBRUCH   1824-1903

Village Scene

Picturesque in setting, with Dutch houses for background of the figures, suffused with lighting which plays upon contrasts, the street gleams fresh washed. People going about their daily chores make it a figure piece as well as landscape.

Water color on paper, $9\frac{1}{4}$ x 12 in. (23 x 30 cm.) Signed in lower left corner: J. H. Weissenbruch.
Gift of Edward Drummond Libbey, 1925.

COLLECTION: Edward Drummond Libbey,   -1925.

JOHANNES BOSBOOM

1817-1891

IN PAINTING the austere interiors of Dutch churches, Bosboom rediscovered the secret of light. To basic craftsmanship as draughtsman and painter of architecture he added keen perception of changing light falling on surfaces of diverse reflective qualities. Early travels in France and Germany, a later trip in Belgium added subjects to the wealth of Dutch material which he interpreted with greatest mastery of his time and place.

INTERIOR OF A DUTCH CATHEDRAL

Simplicity of means, economy of effort, severe restriction of palette, build with telling effect the appearance and atmosphere of a great church. Mastery of perspective, linear and aerial, feeling for composition, sense of light and atmosphere combine to present dignified solemnity of the cathedral, its deep yellow walls and greyed orange and white diapered floor enlivened with occasional notes of brighter color in the costumes and shrine.

Oil on wood, 33⅜ x 26 in. (85 x 66 cm.) Signed at lower left corner: J. Bosboom.

Gift of Edward Drummond Libbey, 1925.

COLLECTION: Edward Drummond Libbey, 1908-1925.

REFERENCES: Museum News, No. 48, March 1926, repr.; Ohio Woman's Magazine, Oct. 1926, repr.

JOHANNES BOSBOOM   1817-1891

Church Interior

Figures give scale to spacious interior; towering walls are illumined by diffused light, their bareness broken by the elaborate carvings, banners, massive chandelier. Characteristic of Bosboom's work is use of soft, melting tones, approaching monochrome, as well as subject and composition. Attention to atmospheric effect shows relation to the contemporary French artists.

Watercolor on paper, 9 x 11 in. (23 x 28 cm.) Signed in lower right corner: J. Bosboom.
Gift of Edward Drummond Libbey, 1925.

Collection: Edward Drummond Libbey,   -1925.

124

JOSEF ISRAELS 1824-1911

PATRIARCH of nineteenth century Dutch painters, most famous and most popular artist of his time and country, Israels was brought up in the academic tradition. Unevenness, ranging from sound technique to careless construction, mars his reputation. In effort to express human feelings he at times approaches sentimentality, at best imparts nobility, dignity of emotion. Frequently monotonous, sometimes hesitant, always sincere, he was admired by Van Gogh, worshipped by lesser lights.

THEIR DAILY BREAD

Figures somewhat hard and tight, carefully composed in sentimental attitude, are set against summary background of rolling dunes dotted with sheep. Adequately portraying surface textures with competent brushwork, forming figures with faultless draughtmanship, the artist has used a cold color scheme of greyed tones. A replica of this picture was in the De Kuyper sale, Amsterdam, May 30, 1911.

Oil on canvas, $49\frac{1}{4}$ x $35\frac{3}{8}$ in. (125 x 90 cm.) Signed in lower left corner: Josef Israels.
Gift of Edward Drummond Libbey, 1914.

COLLECTION: Edward Drummond Libbey, 1901-1914.

EXHIBITION: Toledo Museum, Inaugural, 1912, No. 226, repr. in catalogue.

REFERENCES: Gunsaulus, Josef Israels, An Address Delivered at the Opening of the Exhibition of Josef Israels' Paintings, Toledo Museum of Art, 1912, repr.; Museum News, No. 24, Dec. 1914, repr.

JOSEF ISRAELS

1824-1911

Coming Ashore

One child carries another through shallow water from casually indicated boat to shore. Greyed blue sky and sea form their background. Anecdotal, almost photographic, it intrigues by quaint costume, homely sentiment.

Oil on mahogany, $12\frac{3}{4}$ x $17\frac{3}{4}$ in. (32 x 45 cm.) Signed at lower right: Josef Israels.
Gift of Arthur J. Secor, 1922.

Collection: Arthur J. Secor, 1907-1922.

Exhibition: Toledo Museum, Inaugural, 1912, No. 235, repr. in catalogue.

Reference: Museum News, No. 41, April 1922, repr.

The Parting Day

Frequent portrayal of peasant figures with strong drawing, great solidity, natural attitude gave Israels the title "the Dutch Millet." Drab landscape, fading light enhance effect of toil-begotten fatigue; rhythmic path and swinging figures give sense of plodding motion.

Oil on canvas, $33\frac{1}{4}$ x $16\frac{3}{4}$ in. (84 x 42 cm.) Signed in lower right corner: Josef Israels.
Gift of Arthur J. Secor, 1922.

Collection: Arthur J. Secor, 1907-1922.

Reference: Museum News, No. 41, April 1922, repr.

JOSEF ISRAELS   1824-1911

SELF-PORTRAIT

Posing before his large canvas David Playing before Saul, Israels has executed
his own portrait with firm brush work, freedom of handling, strong characterization, breadth of technique. White of face and beard, grey of hat, black of
suit are admirably set off by subdued but softly glowing colors of background.
Modelling of dominant head proves understanding of structure; flesh tones
and background show appreciation of delicate nuances of color harmony. A
replica exists in the Municipal Museum, Amsterdam, a sketch in the collection
of J. Slagmulder, Amsterdam.

Watercolor on paper, $21\frac{3}{8}$ x 31 in. (54 x 79 cm.) Signed at left: Josef Israels
fecit, for Mr. Libbey 28 Oct. 1908.
Gift of Edward Drummond Libbey, 1914.

COLLECTION: Edward Drummond Libbey, 1908-1914.

EXHIBITIONS: Toledo Museum, Inaugural, 1912, No. 243, repr. in catalogue;
Toledo Museum, Portraits and Portraiture Throughout the Ages, 1937, No. 35.

REFERENCES: Gunsaulus, Josef Israels, An Address Delivered at the Opening of
the Exhibition of Josef Israels' Paintings, Toledo Museum of Art, 1912, repr.;
Eisler, Josef Israels, 1924, repr. Pl. 78; Goldscheider, Five Hundred Self-Portraits,
Vienna, London, 1937, repr. No. 421; Museum News, No. 24, Dec. 1914, repr.

JOSEF ISRAELS   1824-1911

THE NEW FLOWER

A simple domestic scene in typical Dutch interior, this picture is interesting
in play of light through window onto table, flower and standing figure. Fine
drawing, simple composition, unaffected pose of girl, delicate and quiet color
harmonies lend sincere charm and attraction, show capable workmanship.

Watercolor on paper, 9 x 16½ in. (23 x 42 cm.) Signed in lower left corner:
Josef Israels.
Gift of Edward Drummond Libbey, 1925.

COLLECTIONS: E. Laydon Ford; Edward Drummond Libbey,   -1925.

REFERENCES: Gunsaulus, Josef Israels, An Address Delivered at the Opening of
the Exhibition of Josef Israels' Paintings, Toledo Museum of Art, 1912, repr.

JACOB MARIS

STUDY IN France gave him acquaintance with the painters of Barbizon and especial admiration for Daubigny. Painter of landscape and figure, versed equally in oils and watercolor, working for tonal value, veiling color in atmosphere, he became, especially in landscape, an exponent of the planned composition, assembled from many sketches according to rhythmic laws. He and his brothers were the true founders of The Hague school.

SCHEVENINGEN

Cold grey sky is separated from slightly warmer wet grey sands by white-capped breakers. Monotony of color and composition is broken by warmer tones, considered placing of figures and boats.

Oil on canvas, $16\frac{3}{4}$ x $21\frac{3}{4}$ in. (42 x 55 cm.) Signed in lower right corner: J. Maris 1870.
Gift of Arthur J. Secor, 1922.

COLLECTION: Arthur J. Secor, 1909-1922.

THE TOW PATH

Gradations of rich tones of blue and green dominate the color scheme, repetition of foreground colors in lower values in the distance giving depth to the perspective. Fat, juicy impasto applied with vigorous brush lends sparkle and glow. Shadow of dark grey cloud in light blue sky deepens values in landscape. Suggested forms of buildings in the distance, foliage of trees in fore- and middle-ground, head of rider, rise to break skyline. Accomplished color harmonies, well but not obviously balanced composition, technical facility attest mastery of the artist.

Oil on canvas, $15\frac{1}{4}$ x $23\frac{1}{4}$ in. (39 x 60 cm.) Signed in lower right corner: J. Maris.
Gift of Edward Drummond Libbey, 1925.

COLLECTION: Edward Drummond Libbey,   -1925.

JACOB MARIS

1837-1899

BOATS

Quiet, grey-clouded sky and still water are setting for carefully placed boats, their sails forming interesting areas in well-balanced composition, their darker tones relief for almost monochromatic background.

Watercolor on paper, 6½ x 11½ in. (16 x 29 cm.) Signed in lower left corner: J. Maris.
Gift of Edward Drummond Libbey, 1925.

COLLECTION: Edward Drummond Libbey,   -1925.

AMSTERDAM

Views of Dutch towns were favorite subjects, the dominant skyline lending itself to interesting and picturesque treatment. The city, flat, low-lying, occupies but little of the canvas, its taller buildings, the masts and sails of nearby ships carrying up into cloud-filled sky. A low-keyed color scheme ranges from white to grey, intensifying occasional brighter notes appearing in figures, buildings and along the wharf.

Oil on canvas, 31 x 19⅛ in. (79 x 48 cm.) Signed in lower right corner: J. Maris.
Gift of Edward Drummond Libbey, 1925.

COLLECTIONS: J. H. Van Eeghen, Amsterdam; Edward Drummond Libbey, 1908-1925.

REFERENCE: De Bock, Jacob Maris, London, n. d., repr. p. 135.

136

WILLEM MARIS   1844-1910

Youngest of the Maris brothers, taught by the eldest, his range of subject is more limited than that of Jacob and Matthijs. Concentrating on pastoral scenes with animals, he developed broad technique, mellow color, lyric artistry.

Pasture in Sunshine

Light green of pasture, pale blue of sky and water give the tonality of a sunny day, while grey-green of trees, gold-green of reeds and water grasses add varied color notes. Ducks and cows, standard elements in nearly all the artist's works, animate the scene. Constant use of the same theme has conferred perfection of technique, lost feeling and inspiration.

Oil on canvas, 31¾ x 19½ in. (81 x 49 cm.) Signed in lower right corner: Willem Maris f.
Gift of Arthur J. Secor, 1922.

COLLECTION: Arthur J. Secor, 1914-1922.

The Lowlands

Cows in marshy pasture under summer sky are depicted with understanding of nature and animal forms. Greens of lush meadow, golden tones of marsh grasses, hides of cattle, blue of sky, offer chromatic range, emphasize mood of quiet and repose suggested by horizontal lines of composition as well as by subject.

Oil on canvas, 29⅝ x 21⅝ in. (75 x 55 cm.) Signed in lower right corner: Willem Maris.
Gift of Edward Drummond Libbey, 1925.

COLLECTION: Edward Drummond Libbey,   -1925.

138

ANTON MAUVE   1838-1888

INFLUENCED by the Barbizon painters and the Maris brothers, Mauve's popularity, once very considerable, now waned, rests chiefly upon his paintings of sheep. His pictures are dominated by greys and silver tones, his subjects set in the marshlands and on the dunes of his native country, the landscape subordinated to the figures of people, horses, cattle and sheep.

DUTCHMAN SMOKING A PIPE

The stocky figure in battered hat and wrinkled clothes standing on wind-blown dune shows Mauve's facility as draughtsman, his tendency toward dull and greyed colors, his sketchy treatment of landscape reduced completely to background.

Watercolor on paper, 8½ x 12 in. (22 x 30 cm.) Signed in lower right corner: A. Mauve.
Gift of Edward Drummond Libbey, 1925.

COLLECTION: Edward Drummond Libbey,   -1925.

HOMEWARD BOUND

Fall of evening, admirably depicted in golden light near horizon, tinges dull grey clouds with delicate pinks, faint purples, shrouds landscape and figures in shadow. Rider and horses plodding along sodden lane, birds flying low over field suggest end of day's labor. Reflection of sky in pools of water, saturated state of the soil give evidence of the artist's skill, as dampness of atmosphere, wetness of earth proclaim his ability in depiction of light and surface texture.

Oil on canvas, 39⅞ x 26 in. (101 x 66 cm.) Signed at lower right: A. Mauve.
Gift of Edward Drummond Libbey, 1925.

COLLECTION: Edward Drummond Libbey, 1906-1925.

ANTON MAUVE   1838-1888

A DUTCH ROAD

Broken clouds, wet road give Mauve opportunity to show his powers in
depicting the subtleties of grey. Road lined with leafless trees, between ditches
bordered with green grass all provide lines of perspective converging near
center of picture. The animate note is introduced in the woman, horses and
rider.

Oil on canvas, 14½ x 19⅞ in. (37 x 50 cm.) Signed in lower right corner:
A. Mauve f.
Gift of Arthur J. Secor, 1922.

COLLECTION: Arthur J. Secor 1909-1922.
REFERENCE: Museum News, No. 41, April 1922, repr.

SHEEP ON THE DUNES

Basic blue and yellow, much greyed in sky and sheep, combine in loosely
painted grass covering the dunes. Sheep are used chiefly as light-reflecting
surfaces, in complement and contrast to pervading dullness of tone of sky and
pasture. Shepherd and dog contrast with repeated similarity of form, break
gently curving horizontal lines. Ends of over-long composition become dull
and meaningless.

Oil on canvas, 75 x 36½ in. (190 x 93 cm.) Signed in lower right corner:
A. Mauve.
Gift of Edward Drummond Libbey, 1925.

COLLECTIONS: Municipal Museum, Amsterdam (Loan); Edward Drummond
Libbey, 1906-1925.

EXHIBITION: Toledo Museum, Inaugural, 1912, No. 187, repr. in catalogue.

REFERENCES: Singleton, Holland, Chicago, 1908, p. 196, repr.; Preyer, The Art
of the Netherlands Galleries, Boston, 1908, p. 291, repr. Pl. XXXVII.

142

ANTON MAUVE   1838-1888

THE FLOCK

Sheep, their backs light-reflecting, approach and drink from pool in greyed-green pasture under dull sky.

Watercolor on paper, 14 x 20 in. (35 x 51 cm.) Signed in lower right corner: A. Mauve f.
Gift of Edward Drummond Libbey, 1925.

COLLECTION: Edward Drummond Libbey,   -1925.

WOMAN TENDING COW

Against a heavy thicket of young trees well-drawn cow and less competently handled peasant form centers of interest. Light on figures and foremost tree trunks contrasts with shade of grove.

Watercolor on paper, $10\frac{1}{2}$ x $14\frac{3}{8}$ in. (27 x 37 cm.) Signed in lower right corner: A. Mauve f.
Gift of Edward Drummond Libbey, 1925.

COLLECTION: Edward Drummond Libbey,   -1925.

144

ANTON MAUVE   1838-1888

THE WOODCUTTER

Peasant subject reminiscent of Millet, lacking his character and strength, is set against background of logs, dull foliage, neutral sky.

Watercolor on paper, $11\frac{1}{2}$ x $18\frac{1}{2}$ in. (29 x 47 cm.) Signed in lower right corner: A. Mauve.
Gift of Edward Drummond Libbey, 1925.

COLLECTION: Edward Drummond Libbey,   -1925.

146

ALBERT NEUHUIJS   1844-1914

OF THE Hague school and frequently reminiscent of Israels, Neuhuijs, in his early years painter of history, later took as subjects genre scenes—women and children engaged in domestic pursuits in Dutch interiors.

MOTHER AND CHILDREN

Deep warm colors form interesting contrast to cool light on children and mother's apron. Yellow-green basin helps balance colors and masses, shows capable still-life painting.

Oil on oak, $9\frac{1}{4}$ x $12\frac{5}{8}$ in. (23 x 32 cm.) Signed in lower right corner: Albert Neuhuijs.
Gift of Edward Drummond Libbey, 1925.

COLLECTION: Edward Drummond Libbey, 1904-1925.

FRANCOIS PIETER TER MEULEN 1843-

A LESSER light of The Hague school, influenced by Israels, Jacob Maris, Bosboom and Mauve, he is best known for his landscapes with cattle and sheep.

GELDERLAND PASTURES

Greyed color, subject matter, composition show influence of Mauve. Sheep and bare patches of earth give contrast to darker tones of pasturage.

Oil on canvas, $39\frac{1}{2}$ x $28\frac{5}{8}$ in. (100 x 73 cm.) Signed in lower left corner: Ter Meulen.
Gift of Arthur J. Secor, 1922.

COLLECTION: Arthur J. Secor, 1912-1922.

EXHIBITION: Worcester, Mass., Art Museum, 1921.

WILM STEELINK 1856-

An unimportant member of The Hague school, he followed its better known masters, Israels, the Marises and Mauve.

Sheep in Pasture

Peasant's cottage, neighboring trees and fence, balanced by wooded area in the distance add interest, form a composition, as well as a background to the grazing sheep, give greater pictorial effect than usually found in Mauve's more barren canvases. The painting is interesting as the first work of art given the Toledo Museum.

Oil on canvas, 31½ x 21⅜ in. (80 x 53 cm.) Signed in lower right corner: Wilm Steelink; on back of canvas dated 1899.
Gift of Grafton M. Acklin, 1902.

Reference: Museum News, I, January 1908, repr.

152

FRENCH PAINTINGS

Francois Clouet	Elizabeth of Valois
Corneille de Lyon	Marechal Bonnivet
Philippe de Champaigne	Portrait of a Gentleman
Jean Ernest Heinsius	Marquis de Lafayette
Jacques Louis David	Portrait of a Gentleman
Eugene Delacroix	The Return of Columbus
Honore Daumier	Children Under a Tree
Honore Daumier	Head of a Boy
Jean Francois Millet	The Quarriers
Jean Francois Millet	The Gleaner
Jean Francois Millet	The Fagot Gatherer
Jean Baptiste Camille Corot	Canal in Picardy
Theodore Rousseau	In the Auvergne Mountains
Theodore Rousseau	Under the Birches, Evening
Theodore Rousseau	Landscape
Narcisse Virgile Diaz de la Pena	Forest of Fontainebleau
Narcisse Virgile Diaz de la Pena	At the Edge of the Woods
Narcisse Virgile Diaz de la Pena	Deep Woods
Narcisse Virgile Diaz de la Pena	Fontainebleau
Jules Dupre	Landscape
Jules Dupre	Morning
Charles Francois Daubigny	On the River Oise
Charles Francois Daubigny	Clearing After a Storm
Constant Troyon	The Pasture
Constant Troyon	The Cow
Charles Jacque	The Shepherd's Rest
Charles Jacque	Three Sheep
Emile Van Marcke	Cows
Emile Van Marcke	The Pasture Pool
Henri Harpignies	Summer
Henri Harpignies	Mediterranean Coast
Felix Ziem	Golden Venice
Felix Ziem	Venetian Scene
Adolphe Monticelli	The Greyhounds
Jules Breton	The Shepherd's Star

JEAN JACQUES HENNER	THE MAGDALEN AT THE TOMB
GUSTAVE DORE	THE MAN OF SORROWS
GUSTAVE DORE	THE SCOTTISH HIGHLANDS
ADOLPH WILLIAM BOUGUEREAU	THE CAPTIVE
JEAN CHARLES CAZIN	IN THE LOWLANDS
EDOUARD MANET	ANTONIN PROUST
CLAUDE MONET	ANTIBES
EDGAR DEGAS	THE DANCERS
AUGUSTE RENOIR	THE GREEN JARDINIERE
CAMILLE PISSARRO	PEASANTS RESTING
BERTHE MORISOT	IN THE GARDEN
EDOUARD VUILLARD	WOMAN SEATED ON A SOFA
PIERRE BONNARD	THE ABDUCTION OF EUROPA
GEORGES D'ESPAGNAT	THE LEVANDOU
GUSTAVE LOISEAU	THE BANKS OF THE EURE
HENRI MORET	THE SEAWEED GATHERERS
LEON LHERMITTE	NOONDAY REST
GASTON LA TOUCHE	IN THE GARDEN
JOSEPH CLAUDE BAIL	SERVANTS LUNCHING
HENRI LE SIDANER	IN THE GARDEN
VINCENT VAN GOGH	THE WHEAT FIELD
VINCENT VAN GOGH	HOUSES AT AUVERS
PABLO PICASSO	HEAD OF A WOMAN
PABLO PICASSO	WOMAN WITH A CROW
HENRI MATISSE	VASE OF FLOWERS
ANDRE DERAIN	BOATS
ANDRE DERAIN	COMPOSITION
MAURICE DE VLAMINCK	AUVERGNE LANDSCAPE
GIORGIO DI CHIRICO	SELF-PORTRAIT
CHAIM SOUTINE	COLOR ARRANGEMENT
CHAIM SOUTINE	THE VENETIAN
MARIE LAURENCIN	CLOWNS
JULES PASCIN	SEATED GIRL
ROGER DE LA FRESNAYE	PORTRAIT
ROLAND OUDOT	CERES

157

FRANCOIS CLOUET

1516?-1572

FOREMOST French artist of his time, most talented member of a family of painters attached to the court of Francis I in the early sixteenth century, François was son of Jean Clouet, who had come from the Netherlands about 1516. Born at Tours, succeeding his father as valet de chambre and painter to Francis I in 1540, he immortalized his court as his contemporary Holbein did that of Henry VIII of England. He served in succession as painter to four kings, Francis I, Henry II, Francis II, and Charles IX. His works, few of which are signed or dated, are fresh and clear in color, vigorous and accurate in drawing. The Clouets, if not, as they have been called, the founders of the French Renaissance, are certainly among the most important figures in its development.

ELIZABETH OF VALOIS

One of the few great Clouets remaining, probably painted in 1558 or 1559, it may have been the portrait sent to her prospective husband, Philip II of Spain, whom she married in 1559. The face of this fifteen year old princess is modelled with easy touch and great precision; soft lights and shadows play upon delicate coloring of the flesh; severely plain coiffure is graced by an elaborate jewel. In the fashion of the time, rich black dress is heavily embroidered, white sleeves ornamented by slashes. High collar surmounted by ruff underlies jewelled necklace from which hangs an ornate pendant. Splendid color, beautiful line, excellent form, amazing minute detail, enamel-like surface, reveal ability of highest order.

Oil on wood, $9\frac{3}{4}$ x $14\frac{1}{2}$ in. (25 x 36 cm.) Unsigned.
Gift of Edward Drummond Libbey, 1929.

COLLECTIONS: Count de Lonyay (a descendant of Philip II), Nagy-Lonya, Slovakia; Captain Spencer Churchill, London.

EXHIBITIONS: London, Burlington House, French Art, 1932, No. 50, catalogue p. 16, Pl. 22, repr.; Pittsburgh, Carnegie Institute, French Painting, 1936, No. 9, repr. in catalogue; Cleveland Museum, Twentieth Anniversary Exhibition, 1936, No. 187, repr. in catalogue, Pl. XLVIII; Paris, Chefs-d'oeuvre de l'Art Français, 1937, No. 38, repr. Album Pl. 16.

REFERENCES: Konody and Lathom, An Introduction to French Painting, London, 1932, p. 46, repr. as Margaret of Valois; Cent Trente Chefs-d'oeuvre de l'Art Français du Moyen Age au XXe Siècle, Paris, 1937, Pl. 35, repr.; Art News, XXVIII (Nov.

30, 1929), 7, repr. 3;   Museum News, No. 55, Dec. 1929, repr.;   Art Digest, IV (Dec. 15, 1929), 19, repr.;   Parnassus, II (Jan. 1930), 31, repr.;   Beaux-Arts, VIII (Jan. 1930), 7, repr.;   Museion, Paris, IV (1930), 34a, repr.;   Revue de l'Art Ancien et Moderne, LVII (Feb. 1930), 94, repr.;   American Magazine of Art, XXI (Feb. 1930), 107, repr.;   Formes, No. 20, Dec. 1931, 170a-b, repr.;   Fine Arts, XVIII (Jan. 1932), 23, repr.;   Apollo, XV (Feb. 1932), 60, repr.;   Pantheon, IX (March 1932), 88, repr.;   Beaux-Arts, X (Aug. 1932), 76, repr.;   L'Amour de l'Art, XVIII (May 1937), 9, repr.;   L'Art et Les Artistes, XXXV (Feb. 1938), 149, repr.

CORNEILLE, probably born at The Hague, established by 1534 at Lyons, appointed painter to the dauphin, upon his accession as Henri II in 1547 was naturalized and promoted to painter to the king. His name has long represented a style rather than an individual, being attached to numerous small portraits which emanated from his hand, his studio or from others. All follow a definite formula. The face, in three-quarter profile, is set against light green or blue background, frequently darkened at top and one side. Quality varies from badly composed, carelessly drawn effigies to well planned, carefully executed masterpieces, the best being works of rare beauty.

MARECHAL BONNIVET

Carefully considered placing, definite yet delicate modelling, accurate drawing, clear coloring confer great charm and quality. Green background forms excellent foil for black hat and rich velvet garment, harmonious tone with delicate tints of flesh. Light hazel eyes, with fixed piercing gaze, lend vitality, emphasize character. A drawing at Chantilly bearing the name lends credence to traditional identification of the sitter. Technical considerations, notably use of blues in shadows, anticipating Renoir by four centuries, assure Corneille's authorship of this, his largest and finest work.

Oil on wood, 9⅜ x 12⅜ in. (24 x 31 cm.) Unsigned.
Gift of Edward Drummond Libbey, 1938.

COLLECTION: Count Montbrizon, Chateau St. Roche, Montauban.

EXHIBITIONS: Toledo Museum, French and Flemish Primitives, 1935, No. 11, repr.; Cleveland Museum, Twentieth Anniversary Exhibition, 1936, No. 193, repr. Pl. XLVIII.

PHILIPPE DE CHAMPAIGNE 1602-1674

BORN AT Brussels, Champaigne went to France at the age of nineteen, was naturalized in 1629. After working with Poussin under the direction of Duchesne upon the decorations of the Luxembourg for Marie de Medicis, he became painter to the king, professor and director of the Academy. His religious paintings were his most ambitious subjects; history, mythology, and allegory figure in his decorations. His greatness lies in his portraits, the best known being those of Richelieu, whom he painted frequently, Mazarin, Louis XIII, Colbert, and other notables of the time.

PORTRAIT OF A GENTLEMAN

Champaigne combined in portraits the strength of character of his ancestors, the Flemings, the sensitive psychological penetration of his teachers, the French. His large, firm touch, his fine harmony of quiet tones constructs this dignified portrait of a man in black robes relieved by white collar and cuffs of exceptional sheerness. Quiet reserve of the sitter, richness of his costume is set forth by the grey background, brilliant red lining of cloak forming effective accent.

Oil on canvas, 25¾ x 31½ in. (65 x 80 cm.) Unsigned.
Gift of Felix Wildenstein, 1933.

EXHIBITION: Toledo Museum, Portraits and Portraiture Throughout the Ages, 1937, No. 14.

REFERENCES: Art News, XXXII (February 3, 1934), 16, repr.; Museum News, No. 77, Dec. 1936, repr.

164

JEAN ERNEST HEINSIUS

1740-1812

HEINSIUS was born in Germany, studied in Holland, lived the last half of his life in France. From 1772 until 1775 curator of the Grand-ducal Painting Gallery in Weimar, in 1779 he went to Paris. There he began to exhibit, eventually becoming court painter to the daughter of Louis XV. On the outbreak of the French Revolution he returned to Germany, soon was back in Paris, then in Orleans where he remained until his death. Most of his works now known were done in France.

MARQUIS DE LAFAYETTE

Identification of subject is questioned, for there is doubt of correctness of uniform. Precise drawing and definite color characterize the work. Structure of head, modelling of flesh, fine handling of color throughout, all testify to the artist's ability. Yellow, the predominating color, is accentuated by areas of rich blue and red-orange, producing a most striking combination. In keeping with precision of line, brushwork is meticulously smooth and finished.

Oil on canvas, $19\frac{1}{4}$ x $24\frac{1}{2}$ in. (49 x 62 cm.) Signed in upper left corner: Heinsius pinxit.
Gift of Rene Gimpel, 1927.

EXHIBITIONS: New York, Museum of French Art, A Loan Collection of Relics, Curios and Documentary Evidence Relating to the Marquis de Lafayette, 1932, No. 110; Easton, Pa., Lafayette College, Centennial, 1932.

REFERENCES: Brand Whitlock, Lafayette, New York, 1929, II, 314, repr.; Bulletin, Museum of French Art, New York, No. VI, April 1930, p. 14, No. 110, repr. on cover; The Melange, Year Book of Lafayette College, Easton, Pa., 1933, p. 327, repr. p. 345.

166

JACQUES LOUIS DAVID   1748-1825

DESPITE his deficiencies, David remains one of the great figures of French art. Born in Paris, he became the foremost of the painters of the Revolution, the leader of the classical movement. He received the Prix de Rome, and in Italy formed his style under the influence of Roman antiquity. His became the official art of the Revolution and Empire. In 1804 he was appointed first painter to Napoleon, whose reign he immortalized in huge canvases. Upon the Restoration in 1816 he fled to Brussels, where he remained until his death. His classical and historical canvases, monumental in size, are cold, formal and rigid; his portraits show ability of a high order.

PORTRAIT OF A GENTLEMAN

Here are found strong modelling, solid form, accurate draughtsmanship begotten of classical training. Warm tones of the flesh, in which he excelled in all of his portraits, and of the chair are balanced by cool colors in the background and drapery beneath the hand. The face approaches three-dimensional quality of sculpture.

Oil on canvas, 35 x 46 in. (89 x 117 cm.) Signed on table leg at lower right: LD.
Gift of Arthur J. Secor, 1924.

EXHIBITION: Toledo Museum, Portraits and Portraiture Throughout the Ages, 1937, No. 25.

REFERENCE: Museum News, No. 66, Sept. 1933, repr.

EUGENE DELACROIX 1798-1863

LEADER of Romantic revolt against Classicism of David and Ingres, Delacroix learned from Constable reaction of juxtaposed colors, observed long before the Impressionists the law of complementaries. Early trips to England and Morocco formed him, enlarging his horizons, bathing his colors in golden tones of the Orient. Vigorous, prolific, his huge canvases are works of the great decorator, his sketches, smaller paintings, of artist skilled in free handling of brush, imbued with great color sensitivity.

THE RETURN OF COLUMBUS

Painted on commission in 1839 for the Palazzo San Donato, arrangement recalls Titian's Presentation, use of color the rich harmonies of Veronese. Romanticism, evident in choice of subject, is emphasized by introduction of the Indians, the suggestion, through trophies piled in the foreground, of wealth of the Indies. Variety of color is tempered by play of light, distant architecture enhanced by clarity of atmosphere.

Oil on canvas, $33\frac{1}{2}$ x $45\frac{1}{2}$ in. (85 x 116 cm.) Signed in lower left corner: Eug. Delacroix 1839.
Gift of Thomas A. DeVilbiss, 1938.

COLLECTIONS: San Donato Palace; Hollender; Secrétan; Edouard André; Mrs. William A. Slater, New York; Dr. Harold Tovell, Toronto.

EXHIBITIONS: New York, Metropolitan Museum, 1928; New York, M. Knoedler and Co., A Century of French Painting, 1928, No. 9-A, repr. in catalogue; Paris, Louvre, E. Delacroix Exposition, 1930, No. 92; Chicago, Art Institute, Delacroix Exhibition, 1930, No. 23; New York, M. Knoedler and Co., Gros, Géricault, Delacroix, 1938, No. 44, repr. in catalogue.

REFERENCES: Robaut, L'Oeuvre Complete de Eugène Delacroix, Paris, 1885, No. 690, repr.; Catalogue of the Secrétan Sale, Paris, 1889, No. 18, repr.; Moreau-Nelaton, Delacroix raconté par lui-meme, Paris, 1916, I, 192, repr. fig. 181; Pach, The Journal of Eugène Delacroix, New York, 1938, repr. facing p. 272; Art News, XXXVII (Jan. 7, 1939), 16, repr.; Art Digest, XIII (Jan. 15, 1939), 13, 16, repr.; Magazine of Art, XXXII (Jan. 1939), 41, repr.

HONORE DAUMIER

BORN IN Marseilles, early taken to Paris, Daumier manifested artistic talent as a child. Trained by the arduous practice of lithography, which enforced economy and directness, he developed a concentrated, dramatic style. For subject he most frequently chose the Parisian bourgeois. Caricaturist by necessity, he was painter by preference. At once successor of Michelangelo and precursor of the Impressionists, Goya and Cervantes were the inspiration of many of his paintings, the one in technique, the other, with Molière and La Fontaine, in content. His restricted palette is dominated by a few simple tones, the modelling of his figures accomplished by light and shade, the use of bold, broad outline.

CHILDREN UNDER A TREE

Deep blue dress of seated girl, touch of white between her hands, rich red-orange on the figure of standing boy, bright notes of red and pink on cap and shoulder of the second girl enliven sombre tones of foreground, the dominant olive-green of foliage, deep brown of tree trunk. Dense foliage shadows the group, precedes brighter sunlight falling beyond. Solidity of modelling of the sculptor, few but significant lines of the lithographer, emphasize mass, define proportion, render with utmost economy the feeling and sentiment of the scene. Charm of rural childhood is depicted with simplicity and candor.

Oil on canvas, $18\frac{1}{2}$ x $21\frac{7}{8}$ in. (47 x 56 cm.) Signed in lower left corner: H. D. Gift of Edward Drummond Libbey, 1937.

COLLECTION: Katzenellenbogen, Berlin.

REFERENCES: Klossowski, Honoré Daumier, Munich, 1923, p. 132, repr. p. 116, No. 324; Fuchs, Der Maler Daumier, Munich, 1927, p. 48, No. 54a, repr. p. 54; Museum News, No. 79, June 1937, repr.; Art Digest, XI (Sept. 1, 1937), 10, repr.; Art News, XXXV (Sept. 18, 1937), 18, repr.

HONORE DAUMIER

HEAD OF A BOY

Monumentality in miniature is accomplished through largeness of concept, simplicity of modelling, positive drawing, definite outline. High lights, adroitly placed, enliven dark yet warm tones of ruddy flesh, greyed garment, relieve otherwise quiet though luminous quality.

Oil on canvas, $4\frac{5}{8}$ x $5\frac{1}{2}$ in. (12 x 14 cm.) Signed in upper right corner: H. D. Anonymous Gift, 1938.

JEAN FRANCOIS MILLET   1814-1875

BORN a peasant near Cherbourg, Millet consecrated his art to the portrayal of peasants. He, with Daumier and Courbet, became the leaders of the realistic school, a drastic reaction to the romanticism of Géricault and Delacroix which had followed the classicism of David and Ingres. In 1849 he went to Barbizon where he painted for the rest of his life, in but not of the school of Fontainebleau. His work dominated by the human element, he glorified the life and labor of the worker in the fields. His art was of its time, the era which produced the popular revolutions of 1848. He remains one of the greatest and most significant artists of the nineteenth century.

THE QUARRIERS

Diagonal lines, free and dashing brushwork, express strength and effort. Greyed complements, blue-green and red-orange, are the foundation of the color scheme. Few and bold brush strokes suggest rock. Equally bold is the painting of the workmen, splendidly drawn and firmly modelled. Clean, vital color, brilliant technique, easy composition, sound drawing, rank it among the greatest of his works, far superior to others more famous.

Oil on canvas, 23½ x 29 in. (60 x 74 cm.) Signed in lower right corner: J. F. Millet; on back, official seal, Vente J. F. Millet.
Gift of Arthur J. Secor, 1922.

COLLECTIONS: Millet Sale, Paris, 1875, No. 3; Daniel Cottier, Paris; Ichabod T. Williams, New York, (sold, Plaza Hotel, New York, Feb. 3-4, 1915, catalogue No. 100); Arthur J. Secor, 1915-1922.

EXHIBITION: Buffalo, N. Y., Albright Art Gallery, 1932, repr. in catalogue, Pl. 5.

REFERENCES: Museum News, No. 41, April 1922, repr.; Museum News, No. 70, March 1935, repr.; Art Digest, IX (May 1, 1935), 6, repr.

176

JEAN FRANCOIS MILLET   1814-1875

THE GLEANER

Sketch for the standing figure in the famous Gleaners of the Louvre, strength
and character mark each line. A figure of wonderful solidity, the sense of
mass is achieved by simple, sure modelling of the drapery in broad planes and
heavy folds. The dull, almost sombre tones leave it less masterly in color than
in form.

Oil on mahogany, $14\frac{3}{4}$ x $23\frac{3}{4}$ in. (37 x 60 cm.) Signed in lower right corner:
J. F. Millet.
Gift of Arthur J. Secor, 1933.

COLLECTIONS: Madame J. F. Millet; Arthur J. Secor, 1923-1933.

EXHIBITION: Boston, R. C. and N. M. Vose, Barbizon Exhibition, 1908.

REFERENCE: Museum News, No. 70, March 1935.

JEAN FRANCOIS MILLET   1814-1875

THE FAGOT GATHERER

A slight and free sketch, it yet reveals the firm and sure draughtsmanship of
the master. Of a delicate and quiet harmony, it holds to Millet's constant
theme, labor.

Pastel on paper, 11 x 17 in. (28 x 43 cm.) Signed at right: J. F. Millet.
Gift of Edward Drummond Libbey, 1925.

COLLECTION: Edward Drummond Libbey,   -1925.

JEAN BAPTISTE CAMILLE COROT   1796-1875

BORN IN Paris, his training was in the classical school of landscape painting. In 1825, in 1835, and in 1843, he made extended trips to Italy. Influenced by Bonington, Constable and Rousseau, his eyes opened to the charm of the French countryside, his work became the link between the academicism of his predecessors and contemporaries and the impressionism of Monet. Carefully balanced landscapes, firm to the point of hardness, gave place to tonal subjects, atmospheric, evanescent. His portraits, and in less degree, his early landscapes, are interesting chiefly as antecedents of Cézanne. Much of his later life he spent with the Barbizon painters in the forest of Fontainebleau, although his home remained at Ville d'Avray.

CANAL IN PICARDY

Corot preferred delicate aspen, slender poplar, tremulous birch to gnarled oak, majestic elm, sturdy chestnut. He loved nascent foliage of spring, mists of dawn, soft, thickening vapors of evening. In Canal in Picardy grey skies, morning mists are handled with the delicate brushwork notable in his more mature paintings. Foreground, trees, hillside are saturated with color greyed to harmonies of silvery tones; brighter notes are introduced in the nearer figures. Shimmering reflections on water lead to trees occupying the center of the middle ground.

Oil on canvas, $24\frac{1}{4}$ x $18\frac{1}{2}$ in. (62 x 47 cm.) Unsigned; stamped in red, lower right corner: Vente Corot.
Gift of Arthur J. Secor, 1922.

COLLECTIONS: J. Chamouilet, Paris; Marczell de Nemes, Budapest; Arthur J. Secor, 1914-1922.

EXHIBITIONS: Budapest, Musée Beaux-Arts, 1911; Düsseldorf, Museum, 1912.

REFERENCES: Catalogue Corot Atelier Sale, Hôtel Drouot, Paris, March 26, 1875, No. 174, p. 25; Ribaut and Moreau-Nelaton, L'Oeuvre de Corot, Paris, 1905, III, No. 1743, repr.; Museum News, No. 41, April 1922, repr.

THEODORE ROUSSEAU   1812-1867

THE PARISIAN Rousseau was leader of the Barbizon School, which took its name from the village he and his followers made famous. Humiliated by the Salon rejection of two paintings in 1835 he retired to Barbizon to work out his own artistic destiny. Unlike Corot, who derived from Italy and Poussin, he found his inspiration in the Dutch Ruysdael, Hobbema and Van Goyen. Again unlike Corot, his was the scientific rather than the poetic approach to nature. He applied portraiture to landscape, considered the tree an indivdual to be analyzed and interpreted in its permanent, not its transitory characteristics.

IN THE AUVERGNE MOUNTAINS

In this, one of Rousseau's most majestic compositions, interest centers in two great masses of foliage, the heavier at close range, the lighter at a distance. Color and value rhythms form a path which progresses from warm tones of the foreground across middle distance to cool transparency of cloud and blue sky. Detail of foliage is nearly anatomical in its fidelity.

Oil on canvas, $31\frac{7}{8}$ x $25\frac{1}{2}$ in. (81 x 65 cm.) Signed at lower edge toward right: Th. Rousseau 1837.
Gift of Arthur J. Secor, 1922.

COLLECTION: Arthur J. Secor 1912-1922.
REFERENCE: Museum News, No. 41, April 1922.

THEODORE ROUSSEAU 1812-1867

UNDER THE BIRCHES, EVENING

Sometimes called the Village Priest, after the figure which may be found riding along a sunken path beneath the trees, this picture was probably painted about 1842. Against the dark blue sky of evening, golden rays of setting sun illumine trunks and foliage of the birches, while earth sinks into shadow. Pattern of line replaces usual balance of mass; shrouding atmosphere of evening supplants clear definition of day.

Oil on mahogany, $25\frac{3}{8}$ x $16\frac{5}{8}$ in. (64 x 42 cm.) Signed in lower left corner: Th. Rousseau.
Gift of Arthur J. Secor, 1926.

COLLECTIONS: Dr. Veron, Paris, purchased from Rousseau; Henri Didier, Paris; Baron Nathaniel de Rothschild, Paris; George Gould, Paris; Arthur J. Secor, 1926.

EXHIBITIONS: Paris, Galerie Georges Petit, Cent Chefs-d'oeuvre, 1883, No. 82, repr. in catalogue; London, Burlington House, Exhibition of French Art, 1932, No. 498, catalogue p. 112, repr. Pl. 107, No. 348, p. 168, in small edition; Paris, Chefs-d'oeuvre de l'Art Français, 1937, No. 409; Columbus, Gallery of Fine Art, Nineteenth Century French Painting, 1938.

REFERENCES: Catalogue Veron Sale, Hôtel Drouot, Paris, March 17-18, 1858, No. 60; Sensier, Souvenirs sur Th. Rousseau, Paris, 1872, p. 132; Michel, Great Masters of Landscape Painting, London, 1910, p. 320, repr.; Cent Trente Chefs-d'oeuvre de l'Art Français du Moyen Age au XXe Siècle, Paris, 1937, Pl. 94; L'Amour de l'Art, XIII (Jan. 1932), 32, repr. fig. 91; L'Amour de l'Art, XVIII (May 1937), 34, repr.; Museum News, No. 79, June 1937, repr.

LANDSCAPE

Ever dominant in Rousseau's landscape, trees frame quiet pool, extend far into the distance. Their dark forms silhouetted against the pale sky express dignity and power, give to the composition the slow rhythmic movement of nature in quiet mood. Herd and herdsman do not lessen the serenity of the scene.

Oil on mahogany, $24\frac{7}{8}$ x $16\frac{1}{4}$ in. (63 x 41 cm.) Signed in lower left corner: Th. Rousseau.
Gift of Arthur J. Secor, 1935.

COLLECTION: Arthur J. Secor, 1934-1935.

NARCISSE VIRGILE DIAZ DE LA PENA 1808-1876

A MEMBER of the Barbizon group, Diaz was born of Spanish parents in Bordeaux. Aside from serving his apprenticeship to art as a china painter in the Sèvres factory, he was largely self-taught. He aspired to be a figure painter, in which field his eclectic style produced only unimportant works. Developing a facile landscape style under the influence of Rousseau, he was a brilliant but superficial colorist, frequently trusting to his virtuosity to disguise neglect of design.

FOREST OF FONTAINEBLEAU

Handling of trees shows the influence of Rousseau. Clean dark colors contrasted with light tones of sky evoke cool freshness of a shaded wood and trickling stream. Brilliant notes are introduced in figures seated in the foreground.

Oil on mahogany, 29 x $19\frac{7}{8}$ in. (74 x 50 cm.) Signed in lower left corner: N. Diaz 58.
Gift of Arthur J. Secor, 1922.

COLLECTION: Arthur J. Secor, 1906-1922.

EXHIBITION: Columbus, Gallery of Fine Arts, Nineteenth Century French Painting, 1938.

REFERENCE: Museum News, No. 41, April 1922, repr.

AT THE EDGE OF THE WOODS

Rhythms of light and dark areas create interest in a quiet scene. Yellow-green predominates throughout foreground and middle areas; blue is carried from greyed shadows in the road into the brighter tones of sky. The small figure adds human interest.

Oil on mahogany, $30\frac{5}{8}$ x $25\frac{3}{4}$ in. (78 x 65 cm.) Signed in lower left corner. N. Diaz 71.
Gift of Arthur J. Secor, 1922.

COLLECTIONS: Henry Graves, New York (sold 1909); Herman Schauss, New York (sold Jan. 15-17, 1912, catalogue No. 234); Arthur J. Secor, 1912-1922.

REFERENCES: American Art Annual, Washington, 1913, p. 36; Museum News, No. 41, April 1922, repr.

NARCISSE VIRGILE DIAZ DE LA PENA   1808-1876

DEEP WOODS

Diaz affected the paintings of the forest seen from within. He enlivened such canvases by sunlight streaming down the trunk of beech or birch, sparkling upon the moss of a cool glade, or by the introduction of dancing nymphs, Turks or Bohemians, somewhat in the manner of the fêtes galantes of Watteau.

Oil on mahogany, $7\frac{1}{8}$ x $9\frac{1}{2}$ in. (18 x 24 cm.) Signed in lower left corner: N. Diaz.

Gift of Edward Drummond Libbey, 1925.

COLLECTION: Edward Drummond Libbey, 1906-1925.

FONTAINEBLEAU

Sunlight gleams through trees, brilliantly illuminates center of the canvas, in contrast to dark surrounding masses of foliage. Highlights of sun on birch trees break general dark tones of the painting.

Oil on mahogany, 26 x $19\frac{3}{4}$ in. (66 x 50 cm.) Signed in lower left corner: N. Diaz 72.

Gift of Jefferson D. Robinson, 1930.

COLLECTION: Jefferson D. Robinson.

REFERENCE: Museum News, No. 60, June 1931, repr.

190

JULES DUPRE

DUPRE began his career in the Sèvres porcelain factory, left it to visit England, where he became acquainted with Constable, and appeared in the Salon of 1835 as an accomplished artist. He has been called the tragic dramatist of the Barbizon school, while Rousseau was its epic and Corot its idyllic poet. He saw nature in large masses, wisely sacrificed detail to general effect.

LANDSCAPE

Misty atmosphere envelops quiet, simple landscape. Scarcely moving stream in the foreground reflects light of sky, shadow of trees on its bank. Bending figure of a man in the boat, house in the middle distance animate the scene. Oil on canvas, $9\frac{3}{4}$ x 13 in. (25 x 33 cm.) Signed in lower left corner: J. Dupré. Gift of Jefferson D. Robinson, 1930.

COLLECTION: Jefferson D. Robinson.

REFERENCE: Museum News, No. 60, June 1931.

MORNING

Dramatic quality is achieved by strong contrast of light and dark areas, trees, brush, and the far shore being seen against the light in opposition to the high key of the sky. Rich color, strong treatment of form, mark the Barbizon painter, while enamel-like texture is reminiscent of the decorator of porcelain.

Oil on canvas, $26\frac{3}{4}$ x $15\frac{3}{4}$ in. (68 x 40 cm.) Unsigned.
Gift of Arthur J. Secor, 1922.

COLLECTION: Arthur J. Secor, 1909-1922.

REFERENCE: Museum News, No. 41, April 1922, repr.

CHARLES FRANCOIS DAUBIGNY 1817-1878

DAUBIGNY was the son of a landscape painter, began to paint as a child, as a youth made a trip to Italy. The youngest of the Barbizon group, he came there late. Previously he had painted on the river Oise, having established a houseboat studio near Auvers. Reflecting rather than interpreting nature, most of his paintings are rather monotonous, but have a clarity and freshness which foreshadows the Impressionists.

ON THE RIVER OISE

Combination of land, river and sky is Daubigny's chief interest. Rarely are all three not present. Limpid water and greyed reflections of shore and trees give charm; masses appear balanced on the fulcrum of the center tree.

Oil on mahogany, 27 x 14½ in. (69 x 37 cm.) Signed in lower right corner: Daubigny 1865.
Gift of Arthur J. Secor, 1922.

COLLECTIONS: George I. Seney (sold 1891); Charles T. Yerkes, New York (sold 1910); Arthur J. Secor, 1915-1922.

REFERENCES: Catalogue of Collection of Charles T. Yerkes, Esq., New York, 1904, II, No. 32, repr.; Museum News, No. 41, April 1922, repr.

CLEARING AFTER A STORM

Still waters mirror unbroken reflections. Bending rushes and floating ducks shown with light and free brush strokes add life. Moving clouds contrast with the quiet of the landscape below.

Oil on canvas, 37¼ x 26⅛ in. (95 x 66 cm.) Signed in lower right corner: Daubigny 1873.
Gift of Arthur J. Secor, 1927.

COLLECTIONS: Henri Garnier, Paris (sold, Galerie Georges Petit, Dec. 3-4, 1894, No. 22, catalogue p. 7, repr. opp. p. 6); Arthur J. Secor, 1922-1927.

EXHIBITION: Columbus, Gallery of Fine Arts, Nineteenth Century French Paintings, 1938.

CONSTANT TROYON 1810-1865

THOUGH landscape was the first interest of the men of 1830, man and animal frequently found place as accessories in their work. A few reversed the order and gave their chief attention to animate objects. Born at Sèvres, Troyon first painted upon porcelain. A trip to Holland and acquaintance with the work of Paul Potter and Albert Cuyp fixed his career, for thereafter he devoted his talents primarily to the depiction of cattle. An accomplished landscapist with a broad and powerful technique, he was able to introduce the animal into the scene with harmony and strength.

THE PASTURE

Cow and sheep dominate landscape by the painter's able rendering of the glossy coat of the one, the soft texture of the wool of the other as well as by their mass. Reduced almost to a minimum, landscape serves only as background to better emphasize animals by contrast of color and form.

Oil on canvas, $39\frac{3}{4}$ x 32 in. (101 x 81 cm.) Unsigned; stamped in lower right corner, Vente Troyon, within oval.
Gift of Arthur J. Secor, 1922.

COLLECTION: Arthur J. Secor, 1916-1922.
REFERENCE: Museum News, No. 41, April 1922, repr.

THE COW

Harmony of closely related color is emphasized in the picture. Constant attention to similar subject has produced effortless fidelity of representation.

Pastel on paper, $16\frac{1}{2}$ x $21\frac{1}{2}$ in. (42 x 55 cm.) Signed in lower left corner: C. T.
Gift of Edward Drummond Libbey, 1925.

COLLECTION: Edward Drummond Libbey,   -1925.

196

CHARLES JACQUE 1813-1894

THE LAST of the Barbizon painters to survive, Jacque had begun his artistic life as an illustrator. When he joined the painters in the forest of Fontainebleau he began to devote his talents chiefly to the painting of sheep. He had the gift of simplification, which he devoted to good purpose in the representation of the docile and timid animals which mark his canvases. He was the closest friend of Millet.

THE SHEPHERD'S REST

In quiet pastorale, warm sunlight flecks the ground, cool shadows invite repose. Gentle curves of foliage and animals dominate the scheme. Interest divides evenly between landscape and its tenants, between wooded pasture, sheep and their guardian.

Oil on canvas, $26\frac{1}{4}$ x $32\frac{1}{8}$ in. (67 x 82 cm.) Signed in lower left corner: Ch. Jacque.
Gift of Arthur J. Secor, 1922.

COLLECTION: Arthur J. Secor, 1912-1922.
REFERENCE: Museum News, No. 41, April 1922, repr.

THREE SHEEP

Landscape, summarily treated, forms only a sketchy background to its denizens. Play of light and shadow suggests other trees. Rendition of the sheep, faithful to the point of portraiture, is readily distinguished as the artist's chief interest.

Oil on canvas, $12\frac{3}{8}$ x $10\frac{1}{4}$ in. (31 x 26 cm.) Signed in lower left corner: Ch. Jacque.
Gift of Arthur J. Secor, 1922.

COLLECTION: Arthur J. Secor, 1915-1922.
REFERENCE: Museum News, No. 41, April 1922, repr.

198

EMILE VAN MARCKE 1827-1890

TROYON's only pupil, Van Marcké later lived on an estate at Bouttencourt, where he painted and bred fine cattle. He lacked the impressiveness of his master, but produced well-drawn and faithful representations of cows, sheep and other animals.

Cows

The white cow forms the center of interest, others supporting it. A broad view of flat pasture land and active sky serves as background.

Oil on canvas, 25$\frac{7}{8}$ x 19$\frac{7}{8}$ in. (66 x 50 cm.) Signed in lower left corner: Em. van Marcké.
Gift of Edward Drummond Libbey, 1925.

COLLECTION: Edward Drummond Libbey, -1925.

THE PASTURE POOL

Accurately painted cattle, well drawn, firmly modelled, dominate the canvas. Decorative quality is enhanced by the introduction of the mass of trees.

Oil on canvas, 32$\frac{3}{4}$ x 25 in. (83 x 63 cm.) Signed in lower left corner: Em. van Marcké.
Gift of Arthur J. Secor, 1922.

COLLECTION: Arthur J. Secor, 1903-1922.
REFERENCE: Museum News, No. 41, April 1922, repr.

HARPIGNIES, who lived almost a hundred years, carried the Barbizon school into the twentieth century. It is said that he swore only by saint Corot; but while he gained from him a sense of values, he also took from Rousseau his structural strength, and his portraitlike fidelity in the rendering of trees. Born in Valenciennes, he travelled extensively and studied in France, Belgium and Italy.

SUMMER

Water mirrors pale blue of sky. Trees and their shadows repeat forms interesting in pattern. Interlace of branches adds variety. Softness of waving grass gives contrast with stones. Misty distant shore lends attraction. Floating clouds enliven the calm summer sky.

Oil on canvas, 26 x 32⅛ in. (66 x 82 cm.) Signed in lower left corner: H. Harpignies, 1898.
Gift of Arthur J. Secor, 1922.

COLLECTION: Arthur J. Secor, 1907-1922.

REFERENCE: Museum News, No. 41, April 1922, repr.

HENRI HARPIGNIES

1819-1916

MEDITERRANEAN COAST

Corot and Rousseau jointly are antecedent to the trees; the deep blue of the Mediterranean is Harpignies' and nature's own. Sunlight floods the hills, forming delicate pattern. Foreground and foliage are rendered by facile brush; gentle gradations of color permeate the canvas. Solid color, sound draughtsmanship have come from a hand not infirm with age.

Oil on canvas, $25\frac{7}{8}$ x $32\frac{1}{4}$ in. (66 x 82 cm.) Signed in lower left corner: H. Harpignies 1900.
Gift of Arthur J. Secor, 1922.

COLLECTION: Arthur J. Secor, 1909-1922.

REFERENCE: Museum News, No. 41, April 1922, repr.

FELIX ZIEM   1821-1911

ZIEM WAS born in Beaune, son of Hungarian father. A facile improvisor of
exotic tastes, the result of his heritage, he specialized in the depiction of Venetian scenes. He repeated his subject innumerable times, in colors at first sight
iridescent, seductive, dazzling, soon apparent as only bizarre and garish.

GOLDEN VENICE

A view down the Grand Canal, the Doge's palace on one side is balanced by
ships upon the other. Gilded light of dazzling brilliance emanates from the
sky, suffuses the scene.

Oil on canvas, $42\frac{1}{4}$ x $29\frac{1}{2}$ in. (107 x 75 cm.) Signed in lower left corner: Ziem.
Gift of Arthur J. Secor, 1922.

COLLECTION: Ward, New York (sold, American Art Galleries, New York, Jan. 13,
1911, catalogue No. 68).

REFERENCE: Museum News, No. 41, April 1922, repr.

VENETIAN SCENE

The Grand Canal, looking the other way, the Doge's palace is on the right,
Santa Maria della Salute in the distance. Blues, greens, yellows, oranges and
reds juxtaposed intensify each other.

Oil on mahogany, $37\frac{5}{8}$ x $24\frac{3}{4}$ in. (95 x 63 cm.) Signed in lower right corner:
Ziem.
Gift of Jefferson D. Robinson, 1930.

COLLECTION: Jefferson D. Robinson.

REFERENCE: Museum News, No. 60, June 1931, repr.

ADOLPHE MONTICELLI 1824-1886

OF VENETIAN origins, Monticelli was born in Marseilles. He formed his style on Rembrandt, Titian, Veronese, Watteau, Delacroix and Diaz. With the fall of the Second Empire, he quitted Paris for his birthplace, where he lived the remainder of his life. With heavy impasto he poured liquid light and color upon his panels from a palette of such sparkling brilliancy that his colors seemed prepared from crushed jewels. In his work are analogies with Van Gogh, who expressed great admiration for him. He put thought into his work and avoided the temptation to improvise and to repeat himself. His most beautiful canvases, gems half-revealed from the matrix partly cut away, rank him among the important nineteenth century masters.

THE GREYHOUNDS

Drawing reduced to a minimum, seemingly forgotten, the figures have lost their line and are used as masses of color and texture, more brilliant passages in a chromatic symphony. The figures, lacking substance, retaining form, are reduced to decorative elements, ethereal framework for the application of luscious paint.

Oil on mahogany, $21\frac{1}{2}$ x 15 in. (52 x 38 cm.) Signed in lower left corner: Monticelli.
Gift of Arthur J. Secor, 1933.

COLLECTION: Arthur J. Secor, 1923-1933.

JULES BRETON

1827-1906

BRETON studied in Ghent, Antwerp and Paris. For fifty years he devoted himself to idealizing the French peasant in paint. Sentiment and sunset repeat themselves endlessly upon his canvases.

THE SHEPHERD'S STAR

Typical of Breton, the gleaner returns, silhouetted against the landscape. Of Barbizon antecedents, like all his work, it is bathed in a golden glow, reminiscent of the brown tones from which the men of 1830 helped to emancipate art.

Oil on canvas, 30 x $39\frac{7}{8}$ in. (76 x 101 cm.) Signed in lower right corner: Jules Breton 87.
Gift of Arthur J. Secor, 1922.

COLLECTIONS: Art Institute of Chicago, 1889-1908; Arthur J. Secor, 1908-1922.

EXHIBITIONS: Paris Salon, 1888, No. 374; Toledo Museum, Inaugural, 1912, No. 162, repr. in catalogue.

REFERENCE: Museum News, No. 41, April 1922, repr.

JEAN JACQUES HENNER   1829-1905

BORN IN Alsace, Henner studied in Strasburg, Basle and Paris. He was awarded the Prix de Rome. In Italy he came under the spell of Correggio and Giorgione and began to paint those Magdalens and other nude figures enshrouded in mysterious atmosphere from which he derived his fame. Pale nudity crowned with red hair, and set off by a turquoise blue background is his usual formula, and it was only a step from its discovery to its commercial exploitation.

THE MAGDALEN AT THE TOMB

Slender figure of the Magdalen is revealed by blue-green drapery, a color contrast with auburn hair. The same colors, lowered in value, form a background effective in its tonal harmony. Color balanced by contrast, composition relies upon the placing and the long curve of the figure. Religious in subject, handling of the theme lacks significance.

Oil on canvas, $36\frac{3}{4}$ x $48\frac{1}{2}$ in. (93 x 123 cm.) Signed in lower right corner: J. J. Henner 1880.
Gift of Arthur J. Secor, 1930.

COLLECTION: Sarah M. Hitchcock, 1891-1930.

EXHIBITION: Metropolitan Museum of Art (loan), 1891-1930.

REFERENCES: Catalogue, Metropolitan Museum of Art, 1905, p. 73, No. 566; Art News, XXIX (Dec. 6, 1930), 17, repr.; Art News, XXIX (Feb. 7, 1931), 14; Museum News, No. 60, June 1931, repr.; Art Digest, V (Aug. 1931), 12, repr.

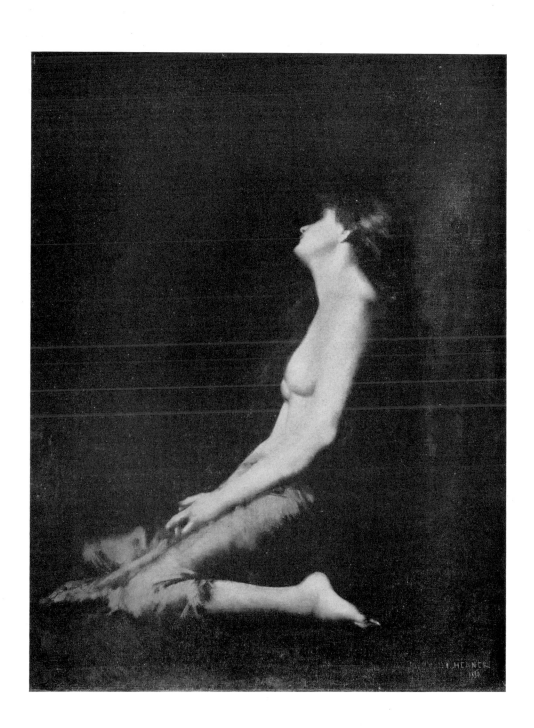

GUSTAVE DORE 1832-1883

DORE, BORN at Strasburg, made his debut as a lithographer there at the age of thirteen. When sixteen he was engaged by the Parisian publisher of the Journal Pour Rire as an illustrator for his magazine. His early caricatures show considerable wit and invention. He turned to historical and literary illustration, wherein he achieved great fame, and made some contributions to technique. He was most prolific, although more of a narrator and inventor than artist. His illustrations are far superior to his paintings.

THE MAN OF SORROWS

Reminiscent of the Italians of the cinquecento, the source and inspiration of Doré's historical and religious painting is clearly evident. Contrasts of expression and attitude of figures against background are overemphasized.

Oil on canvas, $38\frac{5}{8}$ x $48\frac{3}{4}$ in. (98 x 124 cm.) Signed in lower right corner: G. Doré.
Gift of Rene Gimpel, 1923.

THE SCOTTISH HIGHLANDS

Distant mountains are shrouded in mist and obscured by grey clouds. Low trees, bushes and heather cling to the nearer hills. The green water of a mirror-smooth lake lies in the center.

Oil on canvas, 43 x 72 in. (109 x 183 cm.) Signed in lower left corner: Gve. Doré 1875.
Gift of Arthur J. Secor, 1922.

ADOLPH WILLIAM BOUGUEREAU   1825-1905

BOUGUEREAU received the Prix de Rome, and in Italy devoted himself to the decadent masters. In France he was loaded with official honors, not wholly surprising, for he was the best of the legion who were painting the same sort of thing. A master draughtsman, he achieved a style of beauty porcelain-like and impeccable, lacking in feeling, with all other qualities subordinated to grace of line. His tenuous refinement, seldom excelled, in the hands of his countless imitators degenerated into insipidity.

THE CAPTIVE

Before a scenic backdrop of foliage a winged child perched on a marble balustrade holds a captive butterfly at graceful arm's length. Faultless drawing, soft, melting flesh tones mark the nude figure, characteristic of the artist. The empty refinement is not only his, but that of the Second Empire under which he lived.

Oil on canvas, 30½ x 51⅝ in. (77 x 131 cm.) Signed at lower center: W. Bouguereau 1891.
Gift of Sidney Spitzer, 1923.

COLLECTION: Ceilan Milo Spitzer.

216

JEAN CHARLES CAZIN 1841-1901

A WORKER in pastel, he became so imbued with the spirit of that medium that his oils in their pale tints and shades, their light and delicate touch, inescapably suggest the slighter medium. He carried the intimacy of Fantin-Latour and Carrière into landscape. His predilection for twilight, and his fixed preferences in color and tonality create a quality pleasing in one canvas, deadly monotonous in many.

IN THE LOWLANDS

Expanse of cloud-filled sky becomes the dominant feature, windmill and barn picturesque accessories. Colors are softened as by atmospheric haze, harmonized through close values. Facility of technique gives the canvas a superficial effect of breadth.

Oil on canvas, $18\frac{1}{4}$ x $15\frac{1}{8}$ in. (46 x 38 cm.) Signed in lower left corner: J. C. Cazin.
Gift of Edward Drummond Libbey, 1925.

COLLECTION: Edward Drummond Libbey, -1925.

EDOUARD MANET
1832-1883

FORERUNNER and leader of the Impressionist movement, Manet studied with Couture, left his studio to continue his education in the Louvre. There he discovered the Spaniards, especially Velasquez, and upon them founded his style. He travelled to Germany, to Austria, to Italy, to Spain. He soon abandoned shades and shadows and the customary gradation of values to paint in clear tones, juxtaposed without intermediate half tones, and banished gloom from the canvas. After 1870—and an interlude as a staff officer in the Franco-Prussian war under Meissonier—he attacked the problem of sunlight and atmosphere and their effect on color, gave up the stronger contrasts of light and dark. George W. Stevens considered him the greatest of all painters; certainly he was the greatest of his time.

ANTONIN PROUST

Living and vital, enveloping atmosphere of face and figure is recorded with fidelity. Facility of handling does not conceal concept of underlying form nor able drawing. Luminosity of black is the work of genius; dark against dark is most masterly. Effect of light is as strong in highlights of face, collar, hat and coat as could be seen in direct sunlight playing upon open water.

Oil on canvas, 38½ x 51½ in. (98 x 131 cm.) Signed in lower left corner: A mon ami Antonin Proust Manet 1880.
Gift of Edward Drummond Libbey, 1925.

COLLECTIONS: Antonin Proust, Paris; Baron Vitta, Paris; Spier, London.

EXHIBITIONS: Paris Salon, 1880, No. 2450; Paris, Works of Manet, 1884, No. 95; Paris, L'Ecole des Beaux-Arts, Manet Exhibition, 1885, No. 212; Paris, Exposition Centennale de l'Art Français, 1889, No. 492; Paris, Galerie Georges Petit, Exposition des Portraits des Ecrivains et Journalistes, 1893, No. 743; Philadelphia, Pennsylvania Museum, Manet Exhibition, 1933; New York, Wildenstein and Co., Manet, 1937, No. 31, repr. in catalogue, Pl. XXXII; Toledo Museum, Portraits and Portraiture Throughout the Ages, 1937, No. 36.

REFERENCES: Bazire, Manet, Paris, 1884, p. 103, repr.; Duret, Manet and the French Impressionists, Paris, 1902, No. 265; Moreau-Nelaton, Manet Raconté par Lui-meme, Paris, 1926, II, 65, repr. Fig. 261; Tabarant, Manet, Histoire Catalographique, Paris, 1931, p. 367, No. 316; Jamot and Wildenstein, Manet, Paris, 1932, I, 166, No. 376, II, repr. Fig. 110; La Renaissance de l'Art Français, July 1918, p. 153; L'Art et Les Artistes, XXI (Oct. 1930), 26, repr.; Museum News, No. 68, June 1934, repr.

CLAUDE MONET 1840-1926

MOST EMINENT exponent of the aims and aspirations of the Impressionist school, it was the title of one of his works which gave the name to that group. He was conversant with the works of Jongkind and Boudin, precursors of the movement, and inspired by those of Courbet and Corot. Making use of recent scientific theories on the nature of light and color, he discovered the principles and developed the technique which most deeply influenced his associates and successors. Painting with bits of pure color in close proximity Monet and the Impressionists secured new brilliance of color, superior luminosity. Monet made light the subject of his pictures, studying and depicting the infinite variation produced by change of light and atmosphere.

ANTIBES

Harmony of blue, green and yellow, with accents of red and red-orange, the canvas is vibrant with light and color, quiet with the peace of an autumn day. Pattern of trees and distant town take form and substance from subtle contrasts of intensities and values. The more evident and lilting rhythms of tree trunk and branches form a delightful contrast and balance to the reposeful ones of water, town and hills. Shadows are the luminous veils which the Impressionists knew so well how to paint, full of light, but light of a far different quality than that reflected from the direct rays of the sun.

Oil on canvas, $36\frac{1}{2}$ x $29\frac{1}{8}$ in. (93 x 74 cm.) Signed in lower right corner: Claude Monet 88.
Gift of Edward Drummond Libbey, 1929.

COLLECTION: Durand-Ruel, Paris.

EXHIBITIONS: Paris, Centennial Exposition, 1900; London, Grafton Galleries, 1905, catalogue p. 22, repr.; Oberlin, Ohio, Allen Memorial Gallery, 1937.

REFERENCES: Art Digest, III (July 1929), 32, repr.; Art News, XVII (July 13, 1929), 3, repr.; American Magazine of Art, XX (Aug. 1929), 473, repr.; Beaux-Arts, VII (Aug. 1929), 8, repr.; Parnassus, I (Oct. 1929), 20, repr.; Revue de l'Art, Supplement (Bulletin de l'Art, No. 762), LVI (Nov. 1929), 418, repr.; Museum News, No. 56, April 1930.

EDGAR DEGAS 1834-1917

DEGAS added Impressionist color and technique to classic draughtsmanship. Educated at the Ecole des Beaux-Arts and in the Louvre, where he copied Holbein, admired the Italians of the quattrocento and developed a clear concept of design, his first efforts were as painter of historical episode. He made the acquaintance of Ingres whom he so revered that he loved to be called his pupil. Turning from history to his own time, he brought into art new subjects. His great fame rests securely on the dancer and the racehorse, the two most mobile of all creatures. His less frequent subjects, including intimate portraits, have all the elements of greatness.

THE DANCERS

Done in pastel for greater brilliance of color than oil affords, The Dancers represents three ballet girls, shimmering in iridescent color, awaiting their cue. Rhythms of line and color, of angles and curves, of strong yet delicate tones suggest the rhythms of the dance. Seized instantly, the scene is fixed on canvas with no loss of spontaneity. The passion for movement and for life which marked his unprecedented subjects is here in full flower of its beauty. The picture was executed in 1899.

Pastel on paper, mounted on board, 25½ x 24½ in. (65 x 62 cm.) Signed at lower right: Degas.
Gift of Edward Drummond Libbey, 1928.

COLLECTION: Paul Durand-Ruel, Paris.

EXHIBITIONS: London, Grafton Galleries, 1905, No. 64, repr. p. 12, in catalogue; Paris, Galerie Georges Petit, 1924, No. 164;   Philadelphia, Pennsylvania Museum, Degas Exhibition, 1936, No. 56, repr. in catalogue;   Paris, L'Orangerie des Tuileries, Degas Exhibition, 1937, No. 178, repr. in catalogue Pl. XXXII.

REFERENCES: Grappe, Degas, Paris, 1908, p. 31, repr.;   Lafond, Degas, Paris, 1918-1919, II, 30;   Meier-Graefe, Degas, London, 1923, repr. Pl. XCVIII;   Vollard, Degas, New York, 1937, No. 17, repr.;   Mauclair, Degas, Paris, 1937, p. 167, repr. in color Pl. 137, also on paper wrapper;   Art News, XVII (Nov. 1928), repr.;   Art Digest, II (Nov. 1, 1928), repr.;   American Magazine of Art, XVIII (Jan. 1929), repr.;   Museum News, No. 58, Sept. 1930, repr.

AUGUSTE RENOIR
1841-1919

PRODUCT of the Impressionist school, perhaps most representative of the best that lay within it, Renoir was a prodigious worker and prolific painter. As student of Gleyre he knew Monet and Sisley. A year or so later he painted at Fontainebleau with Diaz, and then with Cézanne. He found inspiration in Watteau, Boucher, Delacroix, and for a time in Courbet. His zest for life, his love of the female form, his choice of fat, juicy oil colors, his resolute mastery of technique rank him among the great masters. As painter of the figure, nude or clothed, in outdoor light, he stands supreme.

THE GREEN JARDINIERE

Combining still life and figure—portraiture in a sense, for his wife was the model—it incorporates the artist's most sterling qualities. Broad, free brushwork and rich, brilliant color as background to the pearly tints of flesh which "took the light well," combine in testimony to greatness. Strong greens, deep reds, low in key in the background reinforce the sparkling, brilliant figure of the luscious matron to center interest upon it. It was painted in 1882. Another version exists in the collection of Mr. Harris Whittemore, Jr., Boston.

Oil on canvas, 27 x 36½ in. (69 x 93 cm.) Signed at lower right corner: A. Renoir.

Gift of Edward Drummond Libbey, 1933.

EXHIBITION: Toledo Museum, Portraits and Portraiture Throughout the Ages, 1937, No. 37.

REFERENCES: Meier-Graefe, Renoir, Leipzig, 1929, p. 182, repr. Pl. 152; Art News, XXXII (Feb. 3, 1934), 14, repr.; Art Digest, VIII, (Feb. 15, 1934), 13, repr.; Museum News, No. 71, June 1935, repr.

CAMILLE PISSARRO
1830-1903

FOREMOST among secondary masters of Impressionism, Pissarro was first drawn to Corot and to Millet. Attracted by the new luminism, he allied himself with Monet and its other exponents. Late in life he came under the influence of Seurat, and worked in the Pointillist style. A restless investigator, his work lacks unity, but he had great talent, was a sane thinker, a sound painter, and in his best works approached the genius of his associates. His color, once so brilliant that it offended conservative eyes, has paled in relation to the ever higher keyed works of later painters.

PEASANTS RESTING

Vibrant light suggested by Monet is added to firm drawing and modelling derived from Millet. Sunlight and shadow give brilliant contrast. The canvas radiant with heat as well as light of a summer day, in cool colors suggests refreshing shade of the trees. The individuality of a master in his own right is evident, though simplicity of composition and strength of figures may evidence a debt to Millet, play of light and enveloping atmosphere to Monet.

Oil on canvas, 25¾ x 32 in. (65 x 81 cm.) Signed in lower right corner: C. Pissarro 81.

Gift of Edward Drummond Libbey, 1935.

COLLECTION: Paul Durand-Ruel, Paris.

EXHIBITIONS: New York, Durand-Ruel, 1933; Toledo Museum, Impressionist Exhibition, 1934, No. 14.

REFERENCES: Art News, XXXI (Jan. 7, 1933), repr. on cover; Art News, XXXIII (Feb. 23, 1935), repr. on cover; Museum News, No. 72, Sept. 1935, repr.; Art News, XXXV (July 1937), 16, repr.

BERTHE MORISOT 1841-1895

GRANDDAUGHTER of Fragonard, sister-in-law of Manet, Berthe Morisot painted for diversion, copied old masters in the Louvre, turned to nature, inspired by the aging Corot. In Manet's studio she was converted to luminism. A compound of strength and feminine delicacy, her art combined ephemeral light, the pure outline of reality. Preferring the morning light, whose brilliance blurs form, subdues contrast of light and dark, her subjects were usually in landscape, more rarely under gentler light within doors.

IN THE GARDEN

Forms seem barely sketched, broad painting on second glance revealing substance and mass. Blue-greens of the verdure in varying values emphasize the low intensity yellows and reds of the figures, which through their proximity and contrast in turn strengthen the light blue. Rapidity of brushwork does not lessen solidity of construction.

Oil on canvas, $25\frac{3}{4}$ x $21\frac{3}{8}$ in. (65 x 54 cm.) Signed in lower left corner: Berthe Morisot.
Gift of Edward Drummond Libbey, 1930.

COLLECTION: Lady Cunard, London.

REFERENCES: Museum News, No. 61, Sept. 1931, repr.; The Scroll, Ursuline Academy, Toledo, March 1936, repr.

230

EDOUARD VUILLARD 1867-

EMERGING from his studies with Bouguereau and Robert Fleury at the Academy Julian, Vuillard at length followed the path of the Impressionists, subduing their color, favoring family scenes, interiors quaintly furnished, as more compatible with his restrained palette. His technique, a personal development from that of the early luminists, gives to his paintings texture and quality of tapestry or rug.

WOMAN SEATED ON A SOFA

Composition of the painting as casual as arrangement of the room, costume of the woman—said to be Madame Bernheim, furnishings, decorations, sombre heavy colors, all are reminiscent of the mauve decade. Technique derivative from the Impressionists is altered to fit the pattern of Vuillard's individuality.

Oil on canvas, 45½ x 51½ in. (115 x 131 cm.) Signed in lower right corner: E. Vuillard.
Acquired 1931.

EXHIBITION: Toledo Museum, Portraits and Portraiture Throughout the Ages, 1937, No. 45.

232

PIERRE BONNARD   1867-

TAUGHT by Bouguereau and Robert Fleury, influenced by Manet, Cézanne, Degas, Lautrec, he developed a style of decorative poetic fantasy. In him, combination of academic training with Impressionist inspiration brought compositions of originality, rhythmic charm and grace. In novel arrangement, he has contributed pleasing tonality of strong color.

THE ABDUCTION OF EUROPA

Representation subordinated to rhythms of form and color, brilliant seascape supersedes subject in interest. Opalescence of figures vies with iridescence of waves, both indicative of dazzling brilliance of the Mediterranean sun.

Oil on canvas, $60\frac{1}{2}$ x $46\frac{1}{2}$ in. (154 x 118 cm.) Signed in lower left corner: Bonnard.

Acquired 1930.

EXHIBITIONS: San Francisco, California Palace of Legion of Honor, French Paintings, 1934, No. 61, catalogue p. 43; Pittsburgh, Carnegie Institute, Survey of French Painting, 1936, No. 47.

GEORGES D'ESPAGNAT

1870-

MAKING his debut at the Salon of the Indépendants, D'Espagnat has painted portraits, genre scenes, and landscapes, developing his style on Impressionist foundations. He unites decorative tendencies with clear, harmonious color, leans toward the tones of Renoir.

THE LEVANDOU

Vivid afternoon sun vibrates on sand, boats, houses, figures. Strong, hot colors dominate, relieved by cool, complementary blues. Free impasto, direct balance of color masses, impart interest to simple, homely setting.
Oil on canvas, 36¼ x 29 in. (92 x 73 cm.) Signed in lower left corner: G de E. Acquired 1906.

EXHIBITION: Toledo Museum, One Hundred Impressionist Paintings, 1905, No. 24.

GUSTAVE LOISEAU

LARGELY self-taught, Loiseau joined the ranks of the Impressionists about 1895, too late to be classed as innovator or master, for the problems had been solved, the formulas set. His paintings draw variety from his wide travels, refinement of tone from his technique.

THE BANKS OF THE EURE

Decorative and picturesque, rhythms of form and color spring from use of impressionistic technique. Blue-violet of sky and water echo in the shadows, intensify vivid greens in the foliage.

Oil on canvas, $32\frac{1}{8}$ x $25\frac{7}{8}$ in. (82 x 66 cm.) Signed in lower right corner: G. Loiseau.
Gift of George Durand-Ruel, 1906.

EXHIBITION: Toledo Museum, One Hundred Impressionist Paintings, 1905, No. 33.

HENRI MORET 1856-1913

PUPIL of Gérôme, later coming under the influence of Gauguin, and still later that of Monet, he adopted the Impressionist technique, applying it chiefly to marine painting.

THE SEAWEED GATHERERS

The form of Impressionism shows itself in the vivid, pure colors, the effort to express the atmosphere of seaside life.

Oil on canvas, 26 x 21½ in. (66 x 55 cm.) Signed in lower right corner: Henry Moret 99.
Gift of George Durand-Ruel, 1906

EXHIBITION: Toledo Museum, One Hundred Impressionist Paintings, 1905, No. 59.

LEON LHERMITTE

1844-1925

A PAINTER of peasants, like Millet, he was also the son of a peasant. He derives from Millet in subject rather than in technique, for his works, and particularly the later ones, show the influence of the plein-airists. He received the grand prize at the Paris world exposition in 1889 and again in 1900. At his best, he ranks high in the late nineteenth century French school of naturalism.

NOONDAY REST

Intense blues in sky and on shadowed hill contrast with brilliant tones of orange in noonday sunlight which floods figures, wheat shock and little Gothic church. Interest centers in the artist's typical subject, peasants in their less active moments. A touch of domesticity, frequent with Lhermitte, is added by the man's embrace of his small daughter.

Oil on canvas, 34 x 27½ in. (86 x 70 cm.) Signed in lower right corner: L. Lhermitte 1905.
Gift of Arthur J. Secor, 1922.

COLLECTION: Arthur J. Secor, 1906-1922.

REFERENCE: Museum News, No. 41, April 1922, repr.

GASTON LA TOUCHE

1854-1913

LA TOUCHE was at one time influenced by Manet. Later he turned to the painting of fêtes galantes, continuing the tradition of the eighteenth century decorators. Many of his works show the combination of these two sources of his style.

IN THE GARDEN

Masses of green foliage act as foil to the bright rose dress of the figure. Flickering light and shadow give sparkle and brilliance. Derivative in both subject and technique, disturbing contrast of costume and setting betray eclecticism and virtuosity.

Oil on canvas, 40 x 44 in. (102 x 111 cm.) Signed at lower edge toward right: Gaston La Touche St. C. 02.
Gift of Miss Elsie Mershon, 1926.

COLLECTION: Edward C. Mershon.

JOSEPH CLAUDE BAIL   1862-1921

SON OF A painter, Joseph Bail studied with his father and later with Gérôme
and Carolus-Duran. He became a painter of still life, of interiors with figures,
and of animal pictures. His carefully studied compositions, broadly painted,
are marked by able modelling and harmonious color.

SERVANTS LUNCHING

Bright light falls from the window upon the table and two figures, while a
third figure and the rest of the room are in darkness. Dominant whites are
enhanced by darker tones of the background. Admirable painting of glass,
pottery and brass, as well as figures and the arrangement of lights and darks
show the inspiration of the seventeenth century Dutch painters and acquaintance with Chardin.

Oil on canvas, $53\frac{1}{2}$ x $65\frac{3}{4}$ in. (136 x 167 cm.) Signed in lower right corner:
Bail.

Gift of Edward Drummond Libbey, 1925.

COLLECTIONS: Charles T. Yerkes (sold, April 11-13, 1910, No. 38); Edward
Drummond Libbey, 1910-1925.

246

HENRI LE SIDANER   1862-

BORN OF French parents in Mauritius, he spent his childhood in France, studied with Cabanel. His technique derives from the Pointillist branch of Impressionism. His forms are atmospheric, soft, tenuous, as though seen through a diffusing lens.

IN THE GARDEN

A harmony more of values than of colors, delicate tones in high key suggest shimmering summer sunlight. Composition emphasizes rectangular pattern of door, windows, shutters, softened by play of light.

Oil on canvas, $32\frac{1}{8}$ x $23\frac{7}{8}$ in. (82 x 61 cm.) Signed in lower right corner: Le Sidaner 1891.
Gift of Edward Drummond Libbey, 1925.

COLLECTION: Edward Drummond Libbey,   -1925.

248

VINCENT VAN GOGH 1853-1890

BORN IN Holland, son of a Dutch minister, he gained initial acquaintance with art as employee of a dealer's gallery. He studied with Mauve, copied Millet. His entire meteoric career as painter covered but twelve years, and of these the first eight are negligible. In 1886 he came to Paris. There he was introduced to the Impressionists, to Seurat and Gauguin. At once he wiped the mud of Holland from his palette, reset it with pure pigment fresh from the tube, released the full flood of his volcanic genius for color. Vigorous, powerful designer, Van Gogh devised a forceful harmony of opposed masses of pure tones, unmixed colors; invented rhythms of tortured lines furrowed in the paint with palette knife. Tense, dramatic, profound, his works are the outpouring of his tormented soul, the baring of the mind of a genius of all ages.

THE WHEAT FIELD

Vibrant with light and heat, brilliant green-blue sky and intense yellow field meet in transitional tones of the distant village. The emotional intensity, the passionate enthusiasm of Van Gogh's nature is evident in the quick, nervous line, the vigorous, rhythmic brushwork, the clear, high-keyed color, the vital, strong composition. Painted in the Arles period (1888-89) it is representative of his most dramatic style. A sketch for this painting is in the National Museum, Stockholm.

Oil on canvas, $36\frac{5}{8}$ x 29 in. (93 x 73 cm.) Unsigned.
Gift of Edward Drummond Libbey, 1935.

COLLECTIONS: Leclerq; Gustave Fayet, Igny; Madam d'Andoque, Paris.

EXHIBITIONS: Los Angeles, Museum, Five Centuries of European Painting, 1933, No. 51; Chicago, Art Institute, Century of Progress, 1934, No. 316, repr. in catalogue Pl. XLVIII; Toledo Museum, Impressionist Exhibition, 1934, No. 26; Detroit, Institute of Arts, Van Gogh Exhibition, 1936.

REFERENCES: De la Faille, L'Oeuvre de Vincent Van Gogh, Brussels, 1928, I, 159, No. 559, II, Pl. CLIV, repr.; L'Amour de l'Art, VI, 4, 134, repr.; Gazette des Beaux-Arts, XI (March 1934), 172, repr. Fig. 7; Art Digest, VIII (June 1934), 19, repr.; Art News, XXXIII (Feb. 16, 1935), 8, repr.; Art Digest, IX (March 1, 1935), 13, repr.; Beaux-Arts, part 6, March 15, 1935, repr.

VINCENT VAN GOGH   1853-1890

Houses at Auvers

Removed from the strong Mediterranean light, the softer, greyer illumination of the north governs tone and color. Quieter scene bespeaks calmer treatment. Vigor of handling is undiminished in the straight strokes of house walls and roofs; color applied in rhythmic curves gives strength and character to trees and vines. Blue-violet in roofs, touches of red for flowers confer unexpected harmonies and accents. Painted at Auvers (probably in 1890), it is indicative of his manner at the close of his too brief career.

Oil on canvas, 28¾ x 24 in. (73 x 61 cm.) Unsigned.
Gift of Edward Drummond Libbey, 1935.

COLLECTON: A. Bonger, Amsterdam.

EXHIBITIONS: Amsterdam, Municipal Museum, 1905, No. 209b; New York, Durand-Ruel Gallery, 1934, No. 24; Toledo Museum, Impressionist Exhibition, 1934, No. 25; Detroit, Institute of Arts, Van Gogh Exhibition, 1936; Toronto, Art Gallery, Van Gogh Exhibition, 1936, No. 65a.

REFERENCES: Lettres à son Frère, III, 444, Letter 640; De la Faille, L'Oeuvre de Vincent Van Gogh, Brussels, 1928, I, 214-15, 759, II, pl. CCXII, repr.; Art News, XXXIII (Feb. 23, 1935), 8, repr.; Art Digest, IX (March 1, 1935), 13, repr.; Parnassus, VII (May 1935), 35, repr.

PABLO PICASSO

1881-

SPANISH-BORN, aggressive revolutionary, Picasso founded short-lived Cubism. Schooled by the work of Cézanne, while beguiled by negro sculpture, he sought to express spiritual substance rather than visual form. From reduction to a geometric combination of colored planes he progressed, profiting from his laboratory excursions into the abstract, to sound tactile representation devoid of atmospheric effects of his predecessors. His place in art may be debatable; but no one living has shown more versatile imagination, more inventive genius, and, aside from certain passing and perhaps purely experimental phases of his work, more promise of enduring influence.

HEAD OF A WOMAN

Classical in omission of all but essential elements, sculptural in concept, the features conform to the general character of designed contour. Previous reductions of form to geometric terms have given to Picasso the largeness of vision here evident. It was painted in 1905.

Gouache on paper, mounted on board, 19 x 25⅛ in. (48 x 64 cm.) Signed in upper right corner: Picasso.
Acquired 1931.

COLLECTION: Vollard, Paris.

EXHIBITIONS: San Francisco, California Palace of Legion of Honor, French Paintings, 1934, No. 223, catalogue p. 72; New York, Jacques Seligmann & Co., Picasso Exhibition, 1936, No. 25, repr. in catalogue; Chicago, Art Institute, Watercolors and Gouaches by Picasso, 1937.

REFERENCE: Zervos, Picasso, Paris, 1931, p. xliii, No. 333, repr. p. 156.

PABLO PICASSO

WOMAN WITH A CROW

Scrawny hand, emaciated face evidence Picasso's able drawing. Woman and pet, weird in significance and execution, loom ominous against deep, cold blue of the background. A combination of media, each enhances the other, all unite to produce a work of lasting power, compelling interest, intense penetration.

Gouache on cardboard, $19\frac{1}{8}$ x $25\frac{5}{8}$ in. (50 x 65 cm.) Signed in lower right corner: Picasso 1904.
Acquired 1936.

COLLECTION: Paul Guillaume, Paris.

EXHIBITIONS: Paris, Galerie Georges Petit, 1932, No. 24;   Zurich, Kunsthaus, 1932, No. 22, repr. in catalogue, Pl. IV;   New York, Jacques Seligmann & Co., Picasso Exhibition, 1936, No. 17, repr. in catalogue;   Chicago, Art Institute, Watercolors and Gouaches by Picasso, 1937;   Toledo Museum, Contemporary Movements in European Painting, 1938, No. 89.

REFERENCES: Waldemar George, La Grande Peinture Contemporaine a la Collection Paul Guillaume, Paris, pp. 115, 120, repr. No. 116;   Mahaut, Picasso, Paris, 1930, repr. Pl. 12;   Cahiers d'Art, II (1927), No. 1, repr.

Picasso
1904

HENRI MATISSE   1869-

APOSTLE of Cubism, Matisse had studied under Gustave Moreau, as well as Gérôme and Bouguereau. Attracted in turn by Impressionism, Pointillism, by Gauguin and Cézanne, by Cubism, he developed a personal style. He reflects the modern Near East and residence in Morocco. His paintings are patterns of form and color, simplified into flat planes, into large areas of monotone. His work in the graphic fields shows competent draughtsmanship, not always evident in his paintings, which are frequently uneven, often suggesting variations upon a standard formula.

VASE OF FLOWERS

Curving pattern superimposed upon and in opposition to angular arrangement forms design suggesting influence of the Japanese. More spatial than usual in his work, vase, flowers, table, approach depth and solidity. Cool, pale, harmonious blues, yellows, oranges and greys refresh the eye expectant of his frequent dull, heavy reds, clashing contrast.

Oil on canvas, $32\frac{1}{4}$ x $39\frac{5}{8}$ in. (82 x 101 cm.) Signed in lower right corner: Henri Matisse.
Acquired 1935.

EXHIBITION: Toledo Museum, Contemporary Movements in European Painting, 1938, No. 72.

258

ANDRE DERAIN 1880-

DERAIN emerged from his studies with Carrière, from assimilation of the work of Greco, Van Gogh, Cézanne, from participation in the Fauve movement, with an understanding of volume, an economy of means. His palette, restricted by choice consonant with the simplification of form, consists of deep greens, siennas, ochres, dull reds, iron or pearly greys.

BOATS

An early work, unrepresentative of his most characteristic phases, it evidences the temporary domination of Signac. Brickish reds, dull blues assert pleasing harmony, fall short of luminist aspirations.

Oil on canvas, 39⅛ x 31⅞ in. (99 x 81 cm.) Signed in lower left corner: A. Derain.
Acquired 1931.

EXHIBITION: Paris, Petit Palais, Maîtres de l'Art Indépendent, 1937.

COMPOSITION WITH VIOLIN AND HAT

The facility of a most prolific artist is found in rapid brushstroke, casual composition. Dulled red-orange of short-throated musical instrument is enhanced by rich green of grass, and soft grey of cloth, in its turn accented by deep blue of hat. Unity is achieved through able handling of unusual combination of form and color.

Oil on canvas, 36 x 28½ in. (91 x 72 cm.) Signed in lower right corner: A. Derain.
Acquired 1931.

EXHIBITION: Toledo Museum, Contemporary Movements in European Painting, 1938, No. 29.

MAURICE DE VLAMINCK   1876-

PARISIAN son of Flemish parents, Vlaminck, who was first inspired by Van Gogh, had joined forces with the Fauves by 1908. For a time he and Derain worked together. His work, uneven, and in the mass monotonous from frequent repetition, combines facility and power, is notable for speed and directness of its strong and brilliant technique. Though more aggressively virile, his debt to Cézanne is evident in most of his works.

AUVERGNE LANDSCAPE

Characteristic of his work in rugged handling, simplicity of scene, disregard of perspective, the smudgy brushwork and loose organization often found are absent; nor do the whites resemble cold cream more than paint. In contrast to his frequent theme of bad weather, emphasized by mixture of snow and muddy earth, sunlight and clear atmosphere are depicted with clean paint vigorously applied.

Oil on canvas, $24\frac{1}{8}$ x $19\frac{3}{4}$ in. (61 x 50 cm.) Signed in lower left corner: Vlaminck.
Acquired 1937.

EXHIBITION: Toledo Museum, Contemporary Movements in European Painting, 1938, No. 109.

GIORGIO DI CHIRICO   1888-

BORN IN Greece of Italian parents, Chirico studied in Athens, later in Munich, where he came under the influence of Arnold Böcklin. In Paris in 1911, he exhibited at the Salon d'Automne, the Salon des Indépendants, made the acquaintance of Picasso, who encouraged him to pursue his initial course. He affects heroic horses in combination with fragments of classic architecture against ominous skies, groups of nudes reminiscent of classical or archaic statues. He is abstract in thought rather than in form or design.

SELF-PORTRAIT

Odd combination of sculptured bust facing painted likeness against background of severe architecture and strange sky, its vivid greens reminiscent of Böcklin, the painting is arresting, compelling in its strength and character. Knowledge of the antique is shown in the bust, worthy of a Roman emperor; fine drawing, solid modelling appears in the portrait, a head of strength, vigor, intelligence. Opposing faces, unprecedented, give at once contrast and balance.

Oil on canvas, 20⅛ x 15⅛ in. (51 x 38 cm.) Signed in lower right corner: G. de Chirico se ipsum.
Acquired 1930.

EXHIBITIONS: Iowa City, Iowa, Iowa State University, Figure Paintings, 1936; Toledo Museum, Portraits and Portraiture Throughout the Ages, 1937, No. 52; Toledo Museum, Contemporary Movements in European Painting, 1938, No. 19.

CHAIM SOUTINE 1884-

POLISH, born in Vilna, he came to Paris in 1913. His training academic, his inclinations were Fauvist, Vorticist, perhaps only individualist. With the volubility of his race he pours out expression upon canvas, bending form into approach to abstraction, resolving raw color into flashing, sounding harmonics, erupting vivid, arresting compositions.

COLOR ARRANGEMENT

Dynamic swirls, broad strokes of closely related colors, accented by accurate complements—blues dominant, greens, yellows, oranges subordinate—attain fine balance in a composition surcharged with motion. Semblance of form is subjected to rhythmic pattern of color and texture.

Oil on canvas, $31\frac{7}{8}$ x $43\frac{1}{2}$ in. (81 x 110 cm.) Signed in lower right corner: Soutine.

Gift of I. M. Stettenheim, 1930.

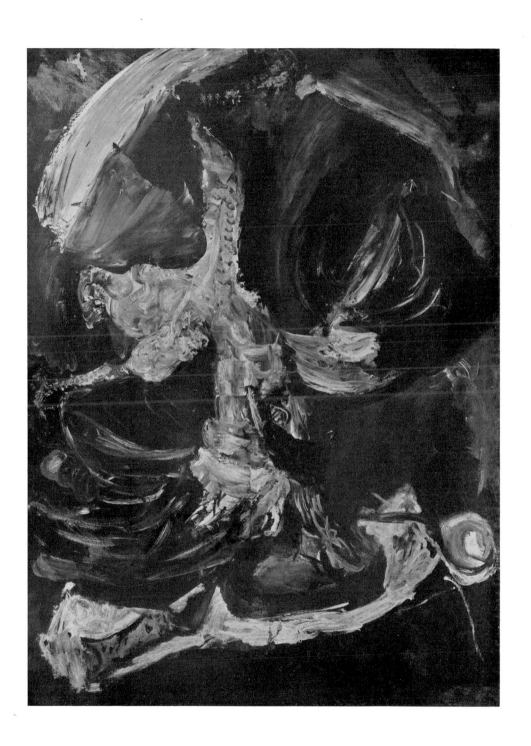

CHAIM SOUTINE   1884-

THE VENETIAN

Colors sombre yet alive, broad impasto model the figure in black dress and hat against dark but vibrant background. Portrait or caricature, forms simplified, distorted to a purpose, dark pools for eyes, heightened color for cheeks, aid characterization, convey distinct impression, mark the type if not the individual.

Oil on canvas, 21½ x 31½ in. (55 x 80 cm.) Signed in lower right corner: C. Soutine.
Acquired 1936.

EXHIBITION: Toledo Museum, Portraits and Portraiture Throughout the Ages, 1937, No. 51.

MARIE LAURENCIN 1885-

CONTINUING the tradition of Berthe Morisot, influenced by Braque and Picasso, Marie Laurençin has created her special type of picture. In flat tones, pastel shades, her paintings have peculiar charm and decorative quality. Reminiscent at once of the Persian miniature and the French rococo, they avoid seriousness, suggest the passing moment, are posterlike, transitory almost to evanescence, adolescent, and most feminine.

CLOWNS

Firm yet free, oil is handled with the quality of opaque watercolor. Flat areas subtly merge to create gentle modelling, to suggest a third dimension. Clear and pure colors derived from the primary triad, high in key; line well conceived and effectively used; values close but distinct; all combine in charming decorative quality.

Oil on canvas, 29 x 36⅜ in. (74 x 92 cm.) Signed in lower left corner: Marie Laurençin 1929.
Acquired 1934.

EXHIBITIONS: Pittsburgh, Carnegie Institute, 1933 International, No. 188, repr. in catalogue, Pl. 59; Cleveland Museum, Foreign Section of 1933 Carnegie International, 1934; Toledo Museum, Foreign Section of 1933 Carnegie International, 1934, No. 32.

JULES PASCIN   1885-1930

BULGARIAN, born of Serbian mother of Italian descent and Spanish father, naturalized an American during the War, he is claimed for France by nature as well as residence. Pupil of Matisse, he has little semblance to his master except a more pronounced predilection for the reclining female form. A thin, dry technique causes many of his oils to approach the wash drawing in appearance. An able draughtsman, he affected looseness of line, even distortion, to obtain animation.

SEATED GIRL

More seated, less sprawled than usual in his work, swiftly, firmly sketched, the figure has substantial form, softness of contour. Delicate harmonies of quiet color, dilute and blended, reduce the sensuality frequently motivating his work.

Oil on canvas, 29 x 36½ in. (74 x 93 cm.) Signed in upper right corner: Pascin.

Acquired 1930.

REFERENCE: Morand, Pascin, Paris, 1931, repr. Pl. 30 (titled Geneviève et le Petit Oiseau).

272

ROGER DE LA FRESNAYE 1885-1925

INFLUENCED first by Cézanne, then by Picasso, La Fresnaye became a follower of the Cubists. Along with most of the others, he deserted their standard when the novelty had worn off, the public amazement ceased. He turned to representational works, reduced to minimum detail.

PORTRAIT

Formal in composition, strong in contrast, almost rigid in balance, the sharp angularity of line is not inharmonious with the subject. Heavy eyebrows, accentuated nose suggest Rouault.

Oil on canvas, 38⅝ x 51½ in. (98 x 131 cm.) Signed in lower right corner: R. de La Fresnaye; inscribed across top of canvas, Georges De Mire.
Gift of I. M. Stettenheim, 1930.

ROLAND OUDOT 1897-

EDUCATED in the School of Decorative Arts, later a teacher there, Oudot worked with Bakst on settings for the Diaghilev Ballet Russe, with Louis Süe and André Mare on interior decorations. He is an exponent of the contemporary style based largely on Cézanne and Picasso.

CERES

A figure solid, static, occupies the center of the canvas against a background of field, trees, and other gleaners. Soft blues dominate the color scheme, textural charm suggests sentiment of the season.

Oil on canvas, $24\frac{1}{4}$ x $39\frac{5}{8}$ in. (61 x 101 cm.) Signed in lower left corner: Roland Oudot.
Acquired 1936.

EXHIBITIONS: Pittsburgh, Carnegie Institute, 1935 International, No. 180; Cleveland Museum, Foreign Section of 1935 Carnegie International, 1936; Toledo Museum, Foreign Section of 1935 Carnegie International, 1936, No. 92.

Roland Oudot

BRITISH PAINTINGS

William Hogarth	Joseph Porter, Esq.
Sir Joshua Reynolds	Sir William Hamilton
Sir Joshua Reynolds	Self-Portrait
Sir Joshua Reynolds	The Hon. Mrs. Watson
Thomas Gainsborough	Lady Frederick Campbell
Thomas Gainsborough	The Shepherd Boy
Thomas Gainsborough	Market Cart
George Romney	Lord MacLeod
Sir Henry Raeburn	Lady Janet Traill
Sir Henry Raeburn	Christina Thomson
Sir Henry Raeburn	Mrs. Bell
John Hoppner	A Lady of the Townshend Family
John Hoppner	Mrs. Gale
Sir Thomas Lawrence	Sir Thomas Frankland
Sir Thomas Lawrence	Countess of Arundell
John Constable	Arundel Mill and Castle
J. M. W. Turner	Venice, The Campo Santo
Sir David Wilkie	H. M. William IV
Walter Greaves	James MacNeill Whistler
Sir John Lavery	Moonlight, Tetuan, Morocco
Frank Brangwyn	The Golden Horn
Philip A. De Laszlo	Edward Drummond Libbey

WILLIAM HOGARTH 1697-1764

MODERN art begins with Hogarth. Lacking an earlier native tradition, uninfluenced by continental trends and fashions, in time, spirit, method, he stands at the beginning of a new era. He knew not the hollow mythology of earlier artists; he ignored the masters of the late Renaissance; he painted the life he saw. Painter, engraver, observer, moralist, his serial pictures are chaptered novels, fulminating sermons, which may be read as well as seen. Yet even in them his prime concern was not precept, satire, invective, but rhythm of flowing line, mellow color.

JOSEPH PORTER, ESQ.

Adequately, inevitably filling the space, the figure, somewhat rigidly posed, shows strength, dignity, character. Contrasting with the cool, greyed greens of coat, greys of hair, are warm flesh tones which are picked up again in ruddy sealing wax, in reflected lights, in heavy curtains in the background. Well-modelled head and arch beyond repeat a graceful curve, contribute to harmony of line, balance of composition. The picture was probably painted not long before 1749.

Oil on canvas, $27\frac{7}{8}$ x $35\frac{3}{4}$ in. (71 x 91 cm.) Unsigned.
Gift of Edward Drummond Libbey, 1925.

COLLECTIONS: Joseph Porter, Esq., of Mortlake, 1749; Miss Lucy Porter, Lichfield, 1786; Rev. J. B. Pearson, 1808; Marquis of Stafford, First Duke of Sutherland, to Fourth Duke of Sutherland, 1814-1913; Lady Millicent Hawes, widow of Fourth Duke of Sutherland, 1913; Edward Drummond Libbey,   -1925.

EXHIBITIONS: London, British Institution, 1814, No. 123; London, British Institution, 1843, No. 171; London, Exhibition of National Portraits, 1867, No. 341, (called Portrait of Captain Coram); London, New Gallery, Exhibition of Royal House of Guelph, 1891, No. 320, (called Portrait of Captain Coram); Toledo Museum, Portraits and Portraiture Throughout the Ages, 1937, No. 18.

REFERENCES: J. Nichols, Biographical Anecdotes of W. Hogarth, 1785, p. 99; Nichols and Steevens, The Genuine Works of William Hogarth, 1808, I, 422-423, II, 286-7, repr.; Trusler, Works of William Hogarth, London, 1827, II, 9; Hogarth, Anecdotes of William Hogarth by Himself, London, 1832, p. 381; Dobson and Armstrong, Hogarth, London, 1902, pp. 185, 188, 232; Dobson, Hogarth, London, 1907, pp. 209, 219, 280; Museum News, No. 80, Sept. 1937.

Engraved by T. Cook, published by Longman, Hurst, Rees & Orme, March 1, 1809.

SIR JOSHUA REYNOLDS

FIRST OF the group whom Hogarth called "portrait manufacturers," Reynolds was the prototype of all society painters since his time. Formed partly by two years in Rome, influenced by Titian, Veronese, Van Dyck, Correggio, his style shows excellencies of composition, technique, superficiality of observation. Incredible industry, punctuality, speed and dexterity provided him an enormous output and income, gave opportunity to deliver his brilliant Discourses, which with his painting deeply influenced the trend of British art. His works always have a surface quality which lends interest and charm; rarely attain that depth and dignity which justify his title to fame.

SIR WILLIAM HAMILTON

Brilliant lighting and strong red of coat, darkened by infinite gradations and surrounded by tones ranging from greyed yellow-greens to black, produce effective though superficial result, characteristic of most of Reynolds' work. Accents of broader brushwork stand out against the smoothly painted finish of the greater portion of the canvas. Painted in 1772 it was renovated by Reynolds in 1785.

Oil on canvas, $25\frac{1}{8}$ x $30\frac{1}{4}$ in. (64 x 77 cm.) Unsigned.
Gift of Edward Drummond Libbey, 1925.

COLLECTIONS: Miss Hamilton, niece of Sir William Hamilton, 1785; Sir W. R. Anson, 1888; Miss F. H. Anson; Edward Drummond Libbey, -1925.

EXHIBITION: London, Royal Academy, 1888, No. 23.

REFERENCES: Cotton, Reynolds, London, 1856, p. 35; Graves and Cronin, Reynolds, London, 1899, II, 424-425, IV, 1329-30; Armstrong, Reynolds, London, 1900, p. 2310; Leslie and Taylor, Reynolds, London, 1867, I, 156, 162, 219; Baldry, Sir Joshua Reynolds, London, n.d., p. xxviii.

SIR JOSHUA REYNOLDS

1723-1792

Self-Portrait

Spontaneity of brushwork and color, strength of drawing, unflattering likeness produce a canvas of life and vitality. Its unpretentiousness and restrained simplicity mark a departure from the usual grandiloquent and decorative portrait of both the age and the artist. Ability in portrayal of character usually sacrificed to the demands of fashion and haste, gives to it an unusual significance. Like Greuze, Reynolds reveals in his self-portraits a certain depth of observation and quality of execution unexpected and rarely encountered in his other works.

Oil on canvas, 25¼ x 30 in. (64 x 76 cm.) Unsigned.
Gift of Edward Drummond Libbey, 1925.

COLLECTION: Edward Drummond Libbey, 1914-1925.

EXHIBITIONS: Cleveland Museum, Inaugural, 1916, No. 25, catalogue p. 122, repr., p. 290; Toledo Museum, Portraits and Portraiture Throughout the Ages, 1937, No. 20.

SIR JOSHUA REYNOLDS 1723-1792

THE HON. MRS. WATSON

Carefully studied yet simple and direct composition of a young matron of twenty-two seated on a garden bench, an alley of trees in the distance, this work embodies the best features of eighteenth century portraiture. Clear flesh tones, rich, creamy white of dress, bright blue of girdle, deep red of cloak edged with black lace, blue-green of bench, are admirably combined, well set off by dark foliage, greyed clouds and sky of background. Accessories of a woman of fashion, flowing decorative line, meticulous treatment of texture do not detract from structural drawing, unified composition. The happy blending of realism and decorative style is characteristic of Reynolds' rare masterpieces. The canvas is one of two replicas of the portrait of Mrs. Watson painted in 1789, both of which were executed soon thereafter.

Oil on canvas, 35⅝ x 45⅞ in. (90 x 155 cm.) Unsigned.
Gift of Arthur J. Secor, 1933.

COLLECTIONS: Sutherland House (?); Forbes-Robertson, London; F. Kleinberger, Paris; Arthur J. Secor, 1923-1933.

EXHIBITIONS: Chicago, Art Institute, Century of Progress, 1933, No. 203, catalogue p. 31, repr.; Toledo Museum, Portraits and Portraiture Throughout the Ages, 1937, No. 19.

REFERENCES: Roberts, Sir Joshua Reynolds's Portraits of the Hon. Mrs. Watson, 1913, (brochure), repr.; Art Institute of Chicago Bulletin, April-May 1933; Connoisseur, XCI (May 1933), 346; Museum News, No. 65, June 1933, repr.; Art News, XXI (August 1, 1933), repr.; Art Digest, VII (August 1, 1933), 9, repr.

THOMAS GAINSBOROUGH 1727-1788

LANDSCAPIST by choice, portraitist by necessity, in both fields Gainsborough rises to surprising heights, sinks to equally surprising depths. Greatest of English, and of eighteenth century European portraitists, as such he shows influence of Van Dyck. As landscapist he first drew inspiration from Hobbema and Ruysdael, later predicted Constable. His work is the abnegation of Reynolds' theorizing, the antithesis of his historical painting. More temperamental, less methodical, far less prolific than Reynolds, he infuses into the best of his work an aristocratic dignity and courtly charm with a light touch, a broad impasto, a rich tonality.

LADY FREDERICK CAMPBELL

Typical of Gainsborough's formal, decorative style of feminine portrait, features are smoothly and subtly modelled, costume, accessories and the dog in her arms quite broadly painted. Yellow of bodice, brown and white of dog give warmth of coloring, break rigidity of pose. Finished suavity, facility of brush attest ability of the artist. Restraint and dignity combine with decorative line and quiet color to produce elegance and nobility. The portrait was probably painted between 1770 and 1775.

Oil on canvas, $25\frac{1}{4}$ x $30\frac{1}{2}$ in. (64 x 77 cm.) Unsigned.
Gift of Arthur J. Secor, 1933.

COLLECTIONS: Baron Curzon, Penn County, Bucks.; Lord Zouche (great-grandson of above); G. L. Bevan, London, 1912-1924; Arthur J. Secor, 1925-1933.

EXHIBITIONS: Cleveland Museum, Inaugural, 1916, No. 5, catalogue p. 119, repr., p. 289 (as Portrait of Lady Ferrers); Toledo Museum, Portraits and Portraiture Throughout the Ages, 1937, No. 21.

THOMAS GAINSBOROUGH 1727-1788

THE SHEPHERD BOY

Idyllic landscape is painted in soft, moist tones, indicating the passing of a storm, also suggested by receding clouds. The distant village is said to be Bamford, near Ipswich, scene of much of Gainsborough's early painting. Typical is the handling of foliage, sheep, bare path. Pattern of interwoven light and dark tones, combination of blue-greens and yellows, fine treatment of perspective give variety and charm.

Oil on canvas, oval, 25$\frac{7}{8}$ x 32$\frac{3}{4}$ in. (66 x 83 cm.) Unsigned.
Gift of Arthur J. Secor, 1933.

COLLECTIONS: Robert Edgar, Colchester; Darrell Brown; Arthur J. Secor, 1926-1933.

EXHIBITIONS: London, British Institution, 1861, No. 214; London, Grosvenor Gallery, 1888, No. 218; Paris, Centennial Exhibition, 1900, No. 48; London, Burlington House, Exhibition of Old Masters, 1903, No. 122.

REFERENCES: Fulcher, Life of Gainsborough, London, 1867, p. 235; Armstrong, Life of Gainsborough, London, p. 205.

Engraved by George Sanders for Henry Graves' Folio of Gainsborough's Works published in 1871.

THOMAS GAINSBOROUGH   1727-1788

Market Cart

In his late style, its free handling, loose, confident brushstroke, skillful balancing of masses, daring use of color demonstrate his mastery, point toward the later development of Constable and all modern landscape. Juxtaposition of greyed cool tones and almost pure warm ones creates scintillant atmospheric quality. Broad and vigorous handling contribute vibrant life. Dog and child introduce interesting anecdote; figures present opportunity for play and contrast of light. Heavy masses of rock and trees in the foreground are balanced by opposed distant view of level water and rising mountain. Complete emancipation from brown tones lies but a step beyond this canvas.

Oil on canvas, 36 x 28$\frac{1}{8}$ in. (91 x 72 cm.) Unsigned.
Gift of Arthur J. Secor, 1933.

COLLECTIONS: Samuel Kilderbee, Ipswich; George Harland-Peck, London.
REFERENCE: Frankau, Mr. Harland-Peck's Collection, Connoisseur, V (Feb. 1903), 85.

GEORGE ROMNEY 1734-1802

HAVING essayed classical and historical subjects, Romney found his place as portraitist. After his return from two years in Italy, his popularity surpassed that of Gainsborough, equalled Reynolds'. Primarily a draughtsman, most dexterous painter of drapery, his grace of line and contour, his happy faculty of never diminishing the beauty of his sitters, while retaining likeness, endeared him to the ladies of his time.

LORD MACLEOD

Standing, three-quarter length, in bright red coat with gold braid, white waist-coat and trousers, white cravat and powdered wig, wearing the ribbon of the Order of the Sword of Sweden, the subject presents a striking and impressive figure. Fine drawing, facile brushwork, high key of color, effective use of line contribute to distinction of the portrait. John MacKenzie, Lord MacLeod, eldest son of third Earl of Cromartie, joined the rising for Prince Charles Edward in 1745, was convicted of high treason, pardoned in 1748. He entered the Swedish military service in 1750, was present at the battle of Prague in 1757 with the Prussian army, returned to England, raised a regiment and served as its Colonel in India, 1779-83, was commissioned Major-General in 1783. This portrait was painted in 1788 and he died in the following year.

Oil on canvas, $40\frac{1}{4}$ x $50\frac{1}{8}$ in. (102 x 128 cm.) Unsigned.
Gift of Arthur J. Secor, 1928.

COLLECTIONS: Hugh Lane, Director of the Dublin Museum; Marquise de Ganay, (sold 1922); Arthur J. Secor, 1925-1928.

EXHIBITIONS: London, Thomas Agnew and Sons, 1913; Toledo Museum, Portraits and Portraiture Throughout the Ages, 1937, No. 22.

REFERENCES: Fraser, The Earls of Cromartie, 1876, I, cclviii-cclxix, lithographed repr.; Ward and Roberts, Romney, London, p. 98; Catrous, Collections de Mme. la Marquise de Ganay, Revue de l'Art, April 1922, pp. 288-291, repr.; Catalogue Marquise de Ganay Collection Sale, Galerie Georges Petit, Paris, May 8-10, 1922, No. 66, repr. opp. p. 70.

COMPLETING his study by two years in Rome, Raeburn returned to Edinburgh, there to become Scotch counterpart of Reynolds, Gainsborough, Romney. As successful with men as with women, he painted in simple, effective manner. His sitters posed with utmost naturalness, his compositions were living and vital, never hard nor affected. He laid on rich paint with vigorous, light, free, sure touch, effecting spontaneity, assuring freshness and charm. Solidity of structure is frequently lacking; directness and intensity are ever present. Modern French paintings frequently recall his concepts of brushwork and color.

LADY JANET TRAILL

The almost monochromatic scheme is composed upon harmonies of yellow, ranging from the pure tone of the bodice through subtle sequences of neutralized, yet warm, luminous tints carried into the background. Notes of greyed blue and delicate flesh tones accent rhythms of color. Broad treatment of flowing, draped costume, summary indication of foliage and receding landscape emphasize clear, cameo-like quality of the features. This picture was painted about 1801.

Oil on canvas, 40¼ x 50¼ in. (102 x 128 cm.) Unsigned.
Gift of Edward Drummond Libbey, 1925.

COLLECTIONS: James Christie Traill, Esq., Castlehill House, Caithness, 1911; Edward Drummond Libbey, 1911-1925.

EXHIBITIONS: New York, Reinhardt Galleries, 1910; Toledo Museum, Inaugural, 1912, No. 199, repr. in catalogue; Cleveland Museum, Inaugural, 1916, No. 22, catalogue p. 122; New York, Reinhardt Galleries, 1927, repr. in catalogue; Toledo Museum, Portraits and Portraiture Throughout the Ages, 1937, No. 28.

REFERENCES: Greig, Sir Henry Raeburn, London, 1911, p. liv, and 61, repr.

SIR HENRY RAEBURN

1756-1823

CHRISTINA THOMSON

Painted about 1822, the year before Raeburn's death, it is interesting as marking the culmination of his artistic career. Elimination of detail, natural simplicity of pose emphasize beauty of face and figure. Clear flesh tones, creamy white of dress, blue-green of wrap, browns of background form pleasing color scheme, while strong lighting and clean shadows intensify contrast of figure with background. Easy, flowing technique here endures to Raeburn's last years.

Oil on canvas, $25\frac{1}{8}$ x $30\frac{1}{8}$ in. (64 x 76 cm.) Unsigned.
Gift of Arthur J. Secor, 1933.

COLLECTIONS: Sir Robert White-Thomson, K.C.B.; Venerable Leonard Jauncey White-Thomson, Archdeacon of Canterbury; Arthur J. Secor, 1922-1933.

EXHIBITION: Toledo Museum, Portraits and Portraiture Throughout the Ages, 1937, No. 29.

REFERENCES: Armstrong, Sir Henry Raeburn, London, 1901, p. 113; Pinnington, Sir Henry Raeburn, London, 1904, p. 253; Greig, Sir Henry Raeburn, London, 1911, p. 62; Roberts, Miss Christina Thomson (Mrs. White) by Sir Henry Raeburn (brochure), London, 1921.

298

SIR HENRY RAEBURN   1756-1823

MRS. BELL

Somewhat earlier than the Miss Thomson, quite similar in arrangement to it, of a less attractive subject, it is less striking in effect. Simplicity, reserve, dignity of concept, broad, fluid painting evidence ability of its author. White dress and red wrap against dark background contribute to decorative effect.

Oil on canvas, 25¼ x 30 in. (64 x 76 cm.) Unsigned.
Gift of Arthur J. Secor, 1933.

COLLECTIONS: W. Hamilton Bell; Arthur J. Secor, 1927-1933.

EXHIBITION: Edinburgh, Royal Scottish Academy, 1880.

REFERENCE: Armstrong, Sir Henry Raeburn, London, 1901, p. 96.

JOHN HOPPNER   1758-1810

DISCIPLE of Reynolds, to some extent his rival, enjoying the royal favor, Hoppner essayed historical, genre, landscape painting, concentrated upon portraiture. Lacking the genius of his greater contemporaries, at his best he painted with decisive stroke, broad brushwork, enveloping his figures in atmosphere which detaches them from the background. More often his work is superficially facile, lacking in solidity of construction, stereotyped in arrangement. His excellences and faults are those of his time and place.

A LADY OF THE TOWNSHEND FAMILY

Traditional column, voluminous drapery, bit of distant landscape form conventional background. Against it refined features of sitter are emphasized by subdued white of gown, grey of coiffure loosely confined by greyed white band and bow. Highly colored flesh tones blend into deeper red of curtains, to which rich dull green of girdle forms interesting opposition. Flowing painting enhances restrained and formal character of portrait. It was probably painted in 1795.

Oil on canvas, 25¾ x 31 in. (65 x 79 cm.) Unsigned.
Gift of Arthur J. Secor, 1933.

COLLECTIONS: Marquesses Townshend, Rainham, Norfolk, from 1795-1904; Major-Gen. Sir Charles Townshend, until 1923; Arthur J. Secor, 1927-1933.

EXHIBITION: Toledo Museum, Portraits and Portraiture Throughout the Ages, 1937, No. 30.

REFERENCE: Roberts, Catalogue Raisonné of John Hoppner's Works, London, 1909, p. 292.

302

JOHN HOPPNER   1758-1810

MRS. GALE

A fresh, youthful subject, mass of loosely coiled auburn hair acts as foil to delicate flesh tones, deep blue of eyes. Simple costume in pale tones shot with dull pinks and blues is sketchily indicated, the background catching and repeating the same hues. Uniformly high key, delicate color, broad though thin technique, confer pleasing harmony, neutralize rigid pose, superficial structure. The subject, Sarah, youngest daughter of Rev. Roger Baldwin, rector of Aldingham, Lancashire, in 1785 married Major, later Lieutenant-General, Henry Richmond Gale of Bardsea Hall, Lancashire. Her portrait was probably painted in 1787.

Oil on canvas, 25⅛ x 30⅛ in. (64 x 76 cm.) Unsigned.
Gift of Edward Drummond Libbey, 1925.

COLLECTIONS: Gen. Henry Richmond Gale, Bardsea Hall, Ulverstone, Lancashire, great-grandson of Mrs. Gale; Edward Drummond Libbey,   -1925.

EXHIBITIONS: London, Thomas Agnew and Sons, 1907, No. 20; New York, Reinhardt Galleries, 1929, No. 17.

REFERENCE: McKay and Roberts, Hoppner, London, 1909, pp. 93-94.

Engraved by T. G. Appleton, 1906.

304

SIR THOMAS LAWRENCE   1769-1830

AN INFANT prodigy, reciting from Shakespeare and Milton at five, painting portraits at a guinea or two each at ten, elected at the behest of George III an associate of the Royal Academy in 1791 before reaching the required age, in the following year he succeeded Reynolds as painter to the king. Tremendously popular, he had as sitters not only the great and fashionable of England, but also the notables of the continent. His superficial, brilliant treatment, equally adapted to depiction of feminine charm and masculine vigor, resulted in portraits of distinction.

SIR THOMAS FRANKLAND

Unexpected realism, utmost simplicity of arrangement dominate the canvas. Ruddy flesh tones are echoed in deeper values in background, set off against black of coat, creamy white of shirt and stock. Strongly modelled face bespeaks character of the individual. Probably painted about 1800, the picture is inscribed at the base "Sir Thos. Frankland B. 1750 O.B. 1831. 6th Baronet, High Sheriff, Yorks: 1792. M. P. Thirsk. 1774-80. 1784-90. 1796-01. Erected Thirkleby House 1782-90. Sir T. Lawrence."

Oil on canvas, 25⅛ x 30⅛ in. (64 x 76 cm.) Unsigned.
Gift of Arthur J. Secor, 1933.

COLLECTION: Arthur J. Secor, 1927-1933.

EXHIBITIONS: Kansas City, Nelson Gallery of Art, English Paintings, 1937; Toledo Museum, Portraits and Portraiture Throughout the Ages, 1937, No. 31.

SIR THOS FRANKLAND
B.1750.S.B. J.S. of 5th... Besworth... Oxon... Vorks: 1792 M.P. Thirsk 1774-80 1784-90 1795-0 ... created a ... 1782 96   SIR T... ...land

SIR THOMAS LAWRENCE 1769-1830

COUNTESS OF ARUNDELL

A portion of a larger painting, once including the seated figure of a man, it is executed with the finished technique for which Lawrence is known. Texture of fabrics, admirably executed in dress, bodice, turban, scarf, supplements and enhances warm flesh tones. Aristocratic bearing and poise are set off against rich curtain and vaguely suggested landscape. The subject was the second wife of James Everard, ninth Baron Arundell of Wardour. This portrait was probably painted soon after her marriage in 1806.

Oil on canvas, $40\frac{1}{4}$ x $50\frac{1}{4}$ in. (102 x 128 cm.) Unsigned.
Gift of Arthur J. Secor, 1925.

COLLECTIONS: Lord Arundell of Wardour Castle, Tisbury, Wilts.; Arthur J. Secor, 1923-1925.

EXHIBITIONS: Buffalo, N. Y., Albright Art Gallery, 1921; Toledo Museum, Portraits and Portraiture Throughout the Ages, 1937, No. 32.

REFERENCE: Academy Notes, Buffalo Fine Arts Academy, Buffalo, XVI (July-Dec. 1921), 53-54, repr.

JOHN CONSTABLE 1776-1837

WITH REVERENT affection, deep respect for nature, the tree, the sky, Constable approached the painting of landscape. Ardent admirer, artistic offspring of Claude, of Ruysdael, of Hobbema, closely akin to Rubens, he first of all painters expressed the flickering light of open air, substituted direct vision of nature for stylized concept. Acclaimed by the French, imitated by the English, he inspired the Barbizon school and the Impressionists, was endlessly reflected in nineteenth century England. His taste was for cultivated landscape, painted in broad masses in the greens of nature. He avoided the browns of his predecessors, giving especial attention to the sky and its changing aspects.

ARUNDEL MILL AND CASTLE

Constable's last painting, in his studio at his death, represents the historic mill and castle at Arundel, long a seat of the Howard family. Diagonal lines of composition lead interest past picturesque mill, along stream, brow of hill, and focus attention upon castle in middle distance. A first step toward Impressionism, glistening verdure adequately indicates luminosity, suggests freshly washed atmosphere. Rich tonal quality unifies green of foliage, red-orange of mill, blues, whites and greys of sky.

Oil on canvas, $39\frac{5}{8}$ x $28\frac{5}{8}$ in. (101 x 72 cm.) Unsigned.
Gift of Edward Drummond Libbey, 1925.

COLLECTIONS: Holbrook Gaskell, 1909; Edward Drummond Libbey, 1909-1925.

EXHIBITIONS: London, Royal Academy, 1837; London, International Exhibition, 1862; London, Burlington House, 1871 and 1885; London, Blackburn Gallery, 1907; New York, Reinhardt Galleries, 1910; Toledo Museum, Inaugural, 1912, No. 164, repr. in catalogue, p. 72; Cleveland Museum, Inaugural, 1916, catalogue p. 119, No. 2.

REFERENCES: Holmes, Constable and his Influence on Landscape Painting, London, 1902, pp. xiv, 217, 222, 252, repr.; Windsor, John Constable, London, 1903, pp. xvi, 145; Leslie, Memoirs of the Life of John Constable, London, 1843, pp. 109, 115; Do., 1845, pp. 283, 292-293; Do., 1937, pp. lxxiii, lxxiv, 353, 356, repr. Pl. 150; Henderson, Constable, London, 1905, pp. 105-106, 112; Lucas, John Constable the Painter, London, 1924, p. 59; Allgemeines Künstler-Lexikon, Leipzig, 1912, VII, 322; Wilenski, Masters of English Painting, Boston, n.d., p. 217; Michel, Histoire de l'Art, Paris, 1925, VIII, 376.

Engraved by David Lucas, S. 49.

310

JOSEPH MALLORD WILLIAM TURNER   1775-1851

PRECOCIOUS child of humble parents, entered at the Royal Academy in time to bask in Reynolds' last effulgence, Turner became a most prolific landscapist. Beginning with wash and watercolor he progressed to oil, produced paintings whose merit was—still is—controversial. He admired, analyzed, imitated Claude Lorrain. Prodigious worker, phenomenal genius, arising without antecedents, departing without decendants, his ardor begat haste of conception, neglect of thoroughness, lack of order. His theatrical, pyrotechnical style, never reduced to formula, resulted at its best in works astounding, at its worst merely astonishing, but always exciting.

VENICE, THE CAMPO SANTO

Companion to the Giudecca, now in the Victoria and Albert Museum, with which it was painted in 1841-42 for Mr. Elhanan Bicknell, this canvas represents Turner at his best. A far cry from the staid Canalettos of similar locale, audacious form is contrived with brilliant color. Clouds erupt rather than hover in the sky. Reflections of boats, sails, low-lying city carry interest into quiet water of foreground. Allure and charm of Venice, its bright but tempered color, brilliant sunlight are instinct in the canvas. Implanted with delicate but firm brush stroke, exquisite use is made of clear blues, pale, warmed yellows, daring touches of brilliant red. Golden rays on clouds are echoed in water. Triumph of Turner's erratic genius, every inch proclaims his mastery.

Oil on canvas, 24⅝ x 36½ in. (62 x 93 cm.) Unsigned.
Gift of Edward Drummond Libbey, 1925.

COLLECTIONS: Elhanan Bicknell, Herne Hall, 1863; Henry McConnell, Cressbrook, Derbyshire, 1886; Mrs. J. M. Keller, Dundee, Scotland; Edward Drummond Libbey,   -1925.

EXHIBITIONS: London, Royal Academy, 1842, No. 73; Manchester, Royal Institution, Art Treasures Exhibition, 1878; London, Guildhall, Turner Exhibition, 1899, No. 36.

REFERENCES: Armstrong, Turner, London, 1902, p. 235; Wyllie, Turner, London, 1905, p. 174, No. 232; Tyrell-Gill, Turner, pp. 155-156; Redford, Art Sales, I, 167, 426-428.

SIR DAVID WILKIE

BORN IN Scotland, of considerable native talent, Wilkie studied in Edinburgh, in London, travelled abroad. His genre paintings, scenes of early nineteenth century English life, were received with acclaim. He followed Lawrence as painter to the king. Lacking strong individuality, his earlier and better subject pictures are influenced by Hogarth, Teniers, Ostade, Rembrandt; his later ones are darkened by Spanish shadow; all are formalized and academic in composition. His portraits, usually excellent, show technical competence.

H. M. WILLIAM IV

High mark of a minor master, the canvas testifies to his ability in skillful brushwork, firm modelling, sound drawing, faithful rendition of textures. Velvet, satin, metal, royal trappings and insignia, carefully yet broadly painted combine to form decorative effect of rare excellence. Face, dwarfed by weight of costume, dominates through breadth of handling, decisive modelling of soft features. Florid flesh tones repeat in softened color the rich red and creamy white of costume.

Oil on canvas, $42\frac{1}{8}$ x $52\frac{1}{8}$ in. (107 x 132 cm.) Unsigned.
Gift of Arthur J. Secor, 1923.

EXHIBITIONS: Buffalo, N. Y., Albright Art Gallery, 1921; Toledo Museum, Portraits and Portraiture Throughout the Ages, 1937, No. 33.

REFERENCES: Academy Notes, Buffalo Academy of Fine Arts, Buffalo, XVI (July-Dec. 1921), 53-55, repr.; Museum News, No. 56, April 1930, repr.; Connoisseur, XCI (March 1933), 181, repr.

WALTER GREAVES

1841?-1930

SELF-TAUGHT, becoming boatman and general assistant to Whistler, he absorbed much from him, reflected his style in portrait and landscape. Etcher as well as painter, he remained unknown until late in life, due to Whistler's injunction to refrain from exhibiting without his permission.

JAMES MACNEILL WHISTLER

Sympathetic rendering of master by pupil, composition is based upon balancing of cold greys, relieved by warmer notes in flesh and tie. Satiric, sardonic personality is well expressed; firm modelling, spatial arrangement, color scheme are reminiscent of the greater artist.

Oil on canvas, $25\frac{1}{8}$ x $30\frac{1}{4}$ in. (64 x 77 cm.) Signed at lower left: W. Greaves 77.
Gift of Carl B. Spitzer, 1910.

REFERENCES: Museum News, IV (Nov. 1910), repr.; Allgemeines Künstler-Lexikon, Leipzig, 1921, XIV, 557.

SIR JOHN LAVERY   1856-1937

IRISH-BORN, student in Glasgow, London, Paris, Lavery came under the influences of Impressionism, Bastien-Lepage, Whistler. His portraits, figure
pieces and landscapes, ranging from brilliantly colored works of precise design
to monochromatic canvases of dark tone and faintly suggested form, evidence
versatility to the point of eclecticism.

MOONLIGHT, TETUAN, MOROCCO

Low-keyed blue, varied in value, judicious and restrained use of touches of
orange, suggest African moonlight on low walls and houses of the town,
dominated by its mosque. Flat pattern of buildings provides contrast to
shadowy, half-concealed form of hills beyond. Firm brushwork of foreground
adds an element of strength.

Oil on canvas, 14⅛ x 25⅛ in. (36 x 64 cm.) Signed in lower right corner:
J. Lavery.
Gift of C. W. Kraushaar, 1912.

REFERENCE: Allgemeines Künstler-Lexikon, Leipzig, 1928, XXII, 476.

FRANK BRANGWYN

TRAINED in the South Kensington art school and William Morris' workshop, profiting from foreign travel and study of continental artists, Brangwyn achieved reputation as draughtsman, etcher, lithographer, painter. Notable either for decorative character of carefully composed areas or deep-toned harmonies of color, his paintings at times approach the jewel-like quality of a Monticelli.

THE GOLDEN HORN

Painted in 1890, after his second visit to the Levant, ships grouped on deep blue Bosphorus form dominating triangular mass near center of composition; buildings gleaming in background offer interesting contrast, substantial balance. Rich color, broadly applied, enhances effect.

Oil on canvas, 30⅛ x 25 in. (76 x 64 cm.) Signed in lower right corner: F. Brangwyn.

Acquired 1931.

COLLECTION: A. G. Kidd, Dundee, Scotland.

EXHIBITION: Wichita, Kansas, Art Association, 1935.

PHILIP A. DE LASZLO   1869-1938

HUNGARIAN by birth, British by naturalization, Laszlo was trained in Budapest, Munich, Paris. Progressing from subject painting to portraiture, he achieved great popularity, became painter of the notable, twentieth century successor of the English eighteenth century portraitists. Through study of them he developed his smooth, all too facile, eclectic style.

EDWARD DRUMMOND LIBBEY

Of clever, capable workmanship, produced in the last years of Mr. Libbey's life, the canvas offers excellent painting, unsatisfactory portraiture. Dramatic use of light and dark forces attention, submerging of unimportant detail in shadow, intensification of flesh coloring gives prominence to face. Failure to grasp and suggest character, despite able handling of medium, leaves the work cold, unimpressive.

Oil on canvas, 36 x 49$\frac{3}{4}$ in. (91 x 126 cm.) Signed in upper right corner: De Laszlo London 1922 Oct.

EXHIBITION: Toledo Museum, Portraits and Portraiture Throughout the Ages, 1937, No. 43.

SWEDISH PAINTINGS

Gustav Adolf Fjaestad	Silence: Winter
Nils Forsberg	Potter at Saint-Amand

RUSSIAN PAINTINGS

V. N. Popoff	The Weaver
Karl N. Kahl	The Old Mill
Karl N. Kahl	End of a Summer Day
Pavel D. Schmaroff	Lady in a Carriage

POLISH PAINTING

Czeslaw Wdowiszewski	Still Life

GUSTAV ADOLF FJAESTAD   1868-

PUPIL of Liljefors and Larsson, Fjaestad is designer of furniture, tapestries, other textiles, as well as painter. Design dominates his work, his subjects being usually winter wilderness, the snow-covered countryside occasionally broken by pools or streams of cold water. His technique is at times suggestive of Signac.

SILENCE: WINTER

Heavy-laden branches form decorative pattern against drifted snow, broken only by trodden path. The gamut of values of blue-violet, intensified in the high lights by slight touches of yellow, shows all the brilliance of color, the subtleties of light and dark which lurk in snow. Simple, unobtrusive technique does not detract from distinctive design, suggestive beauty.

Oil on canvas, 58 x 72 in. (147 x 183 cm.) Signed in lower right corner: G. Fjaestad, 1914, Värmland.
Gift of Edward Drummond Libbey, 1914.

REFERENCE: Museum News, No. 28, Dec. 1915, repr.

NILS FORSBERG 1870-

PARISIAN-BORN son of painter father, Forsberg was educated and worked in France. Painter of portraits and figure pieces, his work shows interest in effect of light traceable to his French predecessors, concern for form derived from his Swedish heritage.

POTTER AT SAINT-AMAND

Contrast of warm light from kiln with cool illumination of shop, both playing upon the jars of wet clay and potter's figure, forms motif of the painting. Variation of values lends interest to the simple scheme of complementary colors. Texture and quality of wet clay is indicated by adequate technique.

Oil on canvas, 51 x 63½ in (127 x 161 cm.) Signed in lower right corner: Nils 1907.
Acquired 1907.

EXHIBITION: Paris, Salon, 1907, No. 636, awarded Honorable Mention.
REFERENCE: Museum News, I, 1, Nov. 1907, repr.

V. N. POPOFF

PRACTICING and teaching painting in St. Petersburg, Popoff developed a style which shows faithful effort combined with some looseness of handling.

THE WEAVER

Sunshine enters dim interior of cabin through a diminutive window, playing upon loom, figure of its operator, wall of logs at her back. Neutralized blues, purples, reds, contrast with bright yellow light of window, together form interesting example of weighing and balancing of colors. Play of shadows enriches the composition.

Oil on canvas, 18 x 26 in. (46 x 66 cm.) Signed in upper right corner: Ben. Popoff 97.
Gift of Harry E. King, 1906.

EXHIBITION: St. Louis, Louisiana Purchase Exposition, 1904, Russian Fine Arts Section, No. 229, awarded Bronze Medal.

REFERENCES: Museum News, I, 3, Jan. 1908, repr.; Clark, Westward to the Pacific, New York, 1935, repr.; Moeller and Moeller, Our Iowa, New York, 1938, p. 257, repr.

KARL N. KAHL
1873-

BORN AT Riga, Kahl studied in Düsseldorf, lived and travelled in Germany, Holland, Belgium and France before returning to Russia. Painter of simple, quiet landscapes, his technique shows sound Düsseldorf training, acquaintance with more progressive movements.

THE OLD MILL

Play of light and shade, rippling reflections, picturesque subject furnish interest and attraction. Use of palette knife enforces breadth of technique.

Oil on canvas, 24 x 32 in. (61 x 81 cm.) Signed in lower right corner: K. N. Kahl.
Gift of Art History Club, 1906.

EXHIBITION: St. Louis, Louisiana Purchase Exposition, 1904, Russian Fine Arts Section, No. 196.

REFERENCES: Scribner's, March 1908, repr.; Museum News, I, 5, March 1908, repr.; Literary Digest, repr. on cover in color; Allgemeines Künstler-Lexikon, Leipzig, 1926, XIX, 434.

END OF A SUMMER DAY

Reflections of deep green, yellow and yellow-green foliage, red tree trunks, saturated with the color of pool in which they are mirrored form transition to blue-purple of open water. A similar gradation exists from heavy impasto of foliage to smoother treatment of pool.

Oil on canvas, 27 x 42 in. (69 x 107 cm.) Signed in lower right corner: K. N. Kahl.
Gift of Robinson Locke, 1906.

EXHIBITION: St. Louis, Louisiana Purchase Exposition, 1904, Russian Fine Arts Section, No. 197, awarded Silver Medal.

REFERENCE: Allgemeines Künstler-Lexikon, Leipzig, 1926, XIX, 434.

PAVEL D. SCHMAROFF

TRAINED at the Academy in St. Petersburg, Schmaroff was chiefly a figure painter, usually choosing peasants in native costume as subjects. His fluid handling was no doubt derived from styles current in western Europe.

LADY IN A CARRIAGE

Considered ultra-modern thirty years ago, modern even today, this large canvas gives surely and strongly the fleeting impression of a momentary glance. Moving traffic of boulevard indicated with great dashing strokes of huge brushes forms background to more clearly and substantially painted figure of woman in the victoria. Great areas of black and swirling greys are enlivened by spots of white, brilliant or mellow, and red of carriage wheel, repeated in varying intensities in lips and beads, reappearing elsewhere, neutralized, in small areas.

Oil on canvas, 57 x 74 in. (145 x 188 cm.) Signed in Russian in lower right corner.

Gift of A. M. Chesbrough, 1906.

EXHIBITION: St. Louis, Louisiana Purchase Exposition, 1904, Russian Fine Arts Section, No. 161, awarded Gold Medal.

REFERENCES: Appleton's Booklovers Magazine, 1904, repr.; Museum News, I, 4, Feb. 1908, repr.; Kondakoff, Jub. Handbook d. St. Petersburg Kstacad. 1764-1914, II, 226 (in Russian); Allgemeines Künstler-Lexikon, Leipzig, 1936, XXX, 128.

CZESLAW WDOWISZEWSKI   1901-

EDUCATED in Warsaw, competent technician, Wdowiszewski has given much attention to the craftsmanship of painting, the chemistry and physics of materials. A precise draughtsman, he paints with clear and accurate detail, high surface finish, achieving brilliancy by a combination of tempera and oil.

STILL LIFE

Laboratory equipment, carefully arranged and studied, faithfully portrayed, is ennobled and enhanced by splendid drawing, smooth, finished painting. Textures are admirably rendered. Predominant yellow-green and low-keyed yellow-orange in the base of the scales form arresting color contrast.

Oil on wood, $17\frac{3}{8}$ x $21\frac{3}{8}$ in. (44 x 54 cm.) Signed in lower left corner: Czeslaw Wdowiszewski 1931.
Acquired 1934.

EXHIBITION: Toledo Museum, Polish Paintings, 1934.

INDEX OF ARTISTS